THE MODERN BOOK
OF RAILWAYS

FOUR-CYLINDER EXPRESS LOCOMOTIVE, " LORD NELSON," SOUTHERN RAILWAY.
  (Photo : Topical Agency.)

This famous locomotive, designed by Mr. R. E. L. Maunsell, was built at the Eastleigh Works in 1926. At the time it was the most powerful passenger express engine in the country.

The four cylinders are 16½in. diameter by 26in. stroke, placed in line under the smoke-box, the inside pair driving the first coupled axle, and the outside pair the second axle. The cranks of the inside and outside cylinders are placed at 45° with one another, so as to obtain a more uniform torque and draught due to the exhaust. Four sets of Walschært valve gears are employed. The high boiler pressure of 220 lbs. per sq. in., together with a Belpaire fire-box and a Maunsell superheater furnish a good reserve of power. With coupled wheels, 6ft. 7in. diameter, it can deal with trains of 500 tons at an average speed of 55 miles an hour over the difficult and heavily graded line between London and Dover. The weight of the engine in working order is 83½ tons. The tender runs on two bogies, and carries 5,000 gallons of water and 5 tons of coal ; its weight in running trim is 56¾ tons.

"MIKADO," 2–8–2 THREE-CYLINDER EXPRESS LOCOMOTIVE No. 2001, " COCK O' THE NORTH," L. & N.E. RAILWAY.   *(Frontispiece.)*   *(Photo : L.N.E.R.)*

The latest design of express engine on the L. & N.E. Railway system is to deal with trains of 550 tons over the Edinburgh-Aberdeen section of the East Coast route, which abounds in heavy grades, and several speed restrictions, and requires spurts of high speeds to keep time. The 2-8-2 wheel arrangement has been adopted so that the wheelbase has not been unduly protracted. The apparent streamlining effect is introduced mainly to raise the exhaust steam clear of the driver's cab, which is V-shaped, to enable a larger spectacle to be fitted and provide what is an excellent look-out. The side sheets form a complete covering, right up to the limits of the construction gauge of the projections on the boiler barrel, and so prevent the smoke eddies forming. The long-shaped dome is covered, and this acts as a steam collector, communicating with the boiler by a number of slots ; it also houses the regulator. In front of the dome are the feed-water heaters' reservoirs. The deep-toned hooter whistle has been placed in front of the double chimney. In working order the total weight of the engine is 110 tons 5 cwts. Three cylinders, each 21in. diameter and 26in. stroke, drive on to coupled wheels, 6ft. 2in. diameter.

The first engine of the class, No. 2001, has rotary cam-operated poppet valves and gear, and the second, No. 2002, *Earl Marischal*, piston valves and Walschært motion. The tender accommodates 8 tons of coal and 5,000 gallons of water ; it is carried on eight wheels, and weighs 55 tons 6 cwts. Engine and tender together, weigh over 165 tons.

THE MODERN
BOOK OF
RAILWAYS

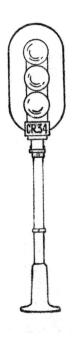

By W. J. BELL, M.I.Loco.E.

A. & C. BLACK Ltd., Soho Square, London, W.1

MADE IN GREAT BRITAIN

Text printed by The London & Norwich Press, Limited, St. Giles Works, Norwich
Illustrations printed by Davy Gravure, Ltd., London

Published Autumn, 1935
Second edition, with an additional chapter, published Autumn, 1938

The United States
THE MACMILLAN COMPANY, NEW YORK

Australia and New Zealand
THE OXFORD UNIVERSITY PRESS, MELBOURNE

Canada
THE MACMILLAN COMPANY OF CANADA, TORONTO

South Africa
THE OXFORD UNIVERSITY PRESS, CAPETOWN

India, Burma, China and F.M.S.
MACMILLAN AND COMPANY, LIMITED
BOMBAY   CALCUTTA   MADRAS

CONTENTS

ILLUSTRATIONS

CHAPTER I

FEW among modern achievements in science and mechanics can offer a more interesting tale of progress and development than our steam railway locomotive. In the following review the examples are arranged largely in chronological order.

The earliest attempts in this country to secure effective application of steam power to the purposes of transport of passengers and goods must be attributed to the need for cheap and efficient carriage of coal from the pits or collieries to the nearest sea-board or canal.

In the history of the steam engine there is no figure so romantic as Richard Trevithick—that wonderful Cornishman, of great stature and strength, the originator of the railway locomotive. Born at Illogan, in 1771, he commenced his career as a mining engineer in 1790. He constructed a high-pressure road locomotive in 1801, the first of its kind; and in conjunction with his cousin, Andrew Vivian, patented a steam road carriage. In 1804 he built a steam locomotive to haul wagons on a tramway from the Pen-y-darren Ironworks, near Merthyr Tydfil, to the Navigation House at Abercynon, on the Glamorganshire Canal, a distance of $9\frac{3}{4}$ miles. This engine weighed about 5 tons, and when tried on February 14th, 1804, hauled 20 tons at a speed of 5 miles per hour. It made several journeys, but was too heavy, and the frequent breakage of the rails soon put an end to the trials. This engine, however, proved that a useful load could be hauled solely by the adhesion of wheels on the track.

In 1808 Richard Trevithick exhibited in London a steam locomotive weighing 8 tons which ran on a circular track at 12 miles per hour. Again trouble was experienced with the track, and nothing further was done by him in connection with the locomotive. He was in advance of his time, and it was left to others to reap the benefits of the adoption of high-pressure steam, of which he was a great advocate.

Richard Trevithick died penniless, unattended by a single relative, at the old Bull Inn, Dartford, Kent, in April, 1833.

Although Trevithick's engines were too heavy for the rails they were too light to secure sufficient adhesion to haul a load large enough to make it a more economical method of traction than horses. To meet this problem, John Blenkinsop, in 1812, had locomotives built for the Middleton Colliery line, Leeds, no heavier than Trevithick's, but provided with cogged driving wheels, which engaged with teeth cast on the rails along one side of the wagon way. They hauled a load five times as great as Trevithick's, although based on the same designs with boilers which had only a single flue.

Towards the end of 1812 William Hedley, viewer at Wylam Colliery, Northumberland, built a more powerful, four-wheeled engine, which had two cylinders and a large boiler fitted with a return flue. This was the famous *Puffing Billy* now in the South Kensington Museum. It also was too heavy, and was rebuilt about 1815 as an eight-wheeler, and altered back to four wheels about 1830, when the line was relaid with heavier rails.

George Stephenson, the most famous of the early locomotive builders, who did more towards improving its construction at its most critical period than anyone else, built his first locomotive in 1814, *Blucher*, at Killingworth, something like Hedley's, but with a boiler containing only a single flue. It hauled eight loaded wagons, about 30 tons, at four miles an hour, on a practically level track. An improvement made was to lead the exhaust steam from the two cylinders to the chimney.

The first public steam railway in the world—the Stockton & Darlington—was authorised in 1821, and George Stephenson was appointed engineer in the following year. After 1822 he devoted his attention mainly to the construction of railways, leaving the development of the locomotive to his son, Robert, and his assistants.

After a time attention was directed to the use of the steam locomotive for passenger and general traffic. A fresh Act was obtained in 1823 by the Stockton & Darlington Railway to carry passengers as well as goods and to employ locomotive engines.

Anticipating a demand for locomotives, the firm of Robert Stephenson & Co. was established at Newcastle-on-Tyne in 1823, and the first engine built by them drew the world's first passenger train at the opening of the S. & D.R., on September 27th, 1825. It was afterwards named *Locomotion No. 1*, and was generally similar to the Killingworth type. Its total weight was $11\frac{1}{4}$ tons in working order; the boiler was 10ft. long and 4ft. in diameter, with a pressure of 25 lbs. per sq. in. There were two vertical cylinders, 9in. bore by 24in. stroke, later enlarged to 10in. diameter. The four wheels were 4ft. in diameter. It hauled 50 tons on the level at five miles an hour. It has been preserved, and now stands on a pedestal on Darlington station platform.

During the next few years many experimental engines were produced and tried on the S. & D. line, and several improvements were made by Timothy Hackworth, its first locomotive superintendent.

When Robert Stephenson returned to England from South America, in 1827, he took steps to simplify the locomotive, reducing its size and improving the details.

The success of the S. & D.R. led to the construction of a railway between Liverpool and Manchester, and George Stephenson was asked to accept the post of engineer. When this line was nearing completion the directors hesitated as to the use of locomotives. To determine whether they were best adapted for traffic on the railway, a prize of £500 was offered for the most efficient locomotive to conform with certain stipulations, chief of which were that the engine should consume its own smoke, be within certain limits of weight, and haul a certain load at ten miles an hour. Five engines were entered for the trials, which commenced on October 6th, 1829, on the Rainhill Level, nine miles from Liverpool ; the *Rocket*, entered by George and Robert Stephenson ; the *Novelty*, by John Braithwaite and John Ericsson ; the *Sans Pareil*, by Timothy Hackworth ; the *Perseverance*, by Timothy Burstall ; and the horse-worked carriage, *Cycloped*, by T. S. Brandreth.

The *Rocket* was a four-wheeled single-driving engine with its cylinders fastened to plates on the boiler, and inclined downwards at an angle of $35°$, so as to drive crank-pins on the front wheels. The cylinders were 8in. diameter by 17in. stroke, and the driving wheels were 4ft. $8\frac{1}{2}$in. diameter. The trailing wheels were 2ft. 6in. diameter, and the wheelbase was 7ft. 2in. The boiler barrel was 3ft. 4in. diameter by 6ft. long and contained 25 copper tubes, 3in. inside diameter. The heating surface was 138 sq. ft. and the grate area 6 sq. ft. The working steam pressure was 50 lbs. per sq. in., and a mercurial gauge indicated the pressure from 45 to 60 lbs. Two safety valves were provided, one loaded by a weighted lever and the other by springs. The exhaust steam passed into the chimney, which was 15ft. high, by two pipes fitted with nozzles 1.5in. diameter.

At Rainhill the *Rocket* was painted yellow and black with a white chimney, the intention being to make the engine look light.

The *Rocket* weighed, with its tender, $7\frac{1}{2}$ tons, and with a load of $12\frac{3}{4}$ tons completed its journey at an average speed of 13.8 miles an hour. It, however, ran light at 29 miles an hour. As it was the only engine to complete the journeys and to fulfil all conditions it was awarded the premium. Its success, mainly due to the adoption of the multi-tubular boiler and the provision of a fire-box, with a water space between the inner and outer shells, together with its simplicity of design, was an important event in locomotive history, as it definitely proved its suitability as a means of general railway haulage, and undoubtedly possessed the chief elements of the modern locomotive. It is now preserved at the South Kensington Science Museum.

The locomotive *Invicta*, delivered to the Canterbury & Whitstable Railway in May, 1830, was built by the Stephensons, and immediately followed the *Rocket*. In 1838 this engine was rebuilt with a cylindrical furnace. It had cylinders 10in. in diameter by 18in. stroke, and 4ft. wheels. It worked at a pressure of 40 lbs. per sq. in., and weighed 6½ tons. It is preserved in the Dane John Garden, at Canterbury.

In connection with the centenary celebrations of the opening of the Liverpool & Manchester Railway, held at Liverpool in September, 1930, the London, Midland & Scottish Railway provided a train of three covered first-class, and three open third-class carriages, built as replicas of the rolling stock used on the line at the time it was opened. This train was hauled by the locomotive *Lion*, of the L. & M.R., and built at Leeds by Todd, Kitson & Laird, in 1838. This old engine was sold by the London & North Western Railway to the Mersey Docks and Harbour Board in 1859, and was used by them as a pumping engine at Prince's Graving Dock, Liverpool, for sixty-nine years. On its withdrawal from service it was restored at Crewe Works in its original form, and provided with a four-wheeled tender. The *Lion* is now exhibited at Lime Street Station, Liverpool, being the property of the Liverpool Engineering Society.

One of the first engines to be regularly employed on the Great Western Railway was the celebrated broad-gauge 7ft. locomotive, *North Star*, constructed by Robert Stephenson & Co., in 1837. It had cylinders 16in. in diameter by 16in. stroke, with " gab " motion, and driving wheels 7ft. diameter. Working pressure 50 lbs. per sq. in. It weighed about 21 tons. Tractive effort 2,070 lbs. This engine was provided with a tender of 750 gallons capacity.

When Isambard Kingdom Brunel, first engineer of the G.W.R., laid out the line from London to Bristol, he adopted a gauge wider

SINGLE DRIVER EXPRESS ENGINE, No. 1, GREAT NORTHERN RAILWAY.

Engine No. 1 of the Great Northern Railway came out in 1870, and is one of Patrick Stirling's celebrated bogie singles with their 8ft. 1in. driving wheels, 18in. by 28in. cylinders, a heating surface of 1,165 sq. ft., and a weight of about 38½ tons, with a tractive effort of 11,245 lbs. The driving wheels carried a weight of 15 tons. These engines performed the greater part of the main-line express work until the end of the nineteenth century. The exceedingly neat outline of these engines, with the domeless boiler and curved roof cab, were notable characteristics.

SINGLE DRIVER LOCOMOTIVE, " CORNWALL," L. & N.W. RAILWAY.

A remarkable engine built in 1847 was Francis Trevithick's " Cornwall," of the London & North Western Railway, with the enormous driving wheels of 8ft. 6in. diameter. As built, the boiler was underneath the axle of the driving wheel, and this was of a most complicated shape. The outside cylinders were 17½in. diameter by 24in. stroke. There were four carrying wheels at the front and two behind the firebox. In 1858 this engine was rebuilt with an ordinary boiler, 4ft. in diameter, above the driving axle. In this form it worked fast trains between Liverpool and Manchester until 1902, and it is still in existence. In its present condition it has a tractive effort of 8,740 lbs.

FRONT-COUPLED PASSENGER LOCOMOTIVE, " GEORGE H. WALLIS," LONDON, BRIGHTON & SOUTH COAST RAILWAY.

Mr. W. Stroudley's famous front-coupled express engines of the London, Brighton & South Coast Railway, always kept clean and smart in their gamboge paint, were very popular with the travelling public. They came out in 1882, and had 18¼in. by 26in. cylinders and 6ft. 6in. wheels, and were known as the " Gladstone " class.

Designed for the service between London and Brighton, these engines gained an excellent reputation for punctual working. At that date the most important train running from Brighton to London, the 8.45 a.m., was allowed one hour and ten minutes, the distance being 50½ miles. The return train left London Bridge at 5 p.m. and arrived at Brighton at 6.5 p.m., or at an average speed of 46.5 miles an hour. The weight of the train was 245 tons.

SINGLE DRIVER BROAD-GAUGE LOCOMOTIVE, " EUPATORIA," GREAT WESTERN RAILWAY.

The broad-gauge locomotive, " Eupatoria," was built at the Swindon Works of the Great Western Railway in 1878, it being one of a series of six engines built to replace a number of similar type designed by Sir Daniel Gooch in the " 'fifties." Gooch link motion was fitted, and the cylinders were 18in. diameter by 24in. stroke, the boiler pressure being 140 lbs., and the driving wheels 8ft. diameter.

Twenty-three of these engines were at work on the fast main line trains in May, 1892, when the 7ft. gauge ceased to exist.

STREAM-LINED " KING " CLASS LOCOMOTIVE, No. 6014, " KING HENRY VII," GREAT WESTERN RAILWAY.

One of the four-cylinder 4-6-0 express passenger " King " class locomotives of the Great Western Railway has been fitted with streamline screens and deflectors, with the object of reducing wind resistance and effecting economy in coal consumption. These engines have four cylinders 16¼in. diameter by 28in. stroke and 6ft. 6in. driving wheels, the tractive effort being 40,300 lbs. The steam pressure is 250 lbs. per sq. in.

4-4-0 PASSENGER ENGINE, No. 336, L. & N.E. RAILWAY, WITH ROTARY CAM POPPET VALVE GEAR.

For service in the North East of England and Scotland a powerful class of three-cylinder 4-4-0 express locomotive has been adopted. The first series of twenty-eight built at Darlington Works was named after the " Shires," and these have been followed by a further forty, which have been named after the " Hunts " in the districts served by the L. & N.E. Railway. The three cylinders are 17in. diameter, with a stroke of 26in., arranged in line horizontally and served by poppet valves operated by rotary cams. They have coupled wheels, 6ft. 8in. diameter, carrying a working pressure of 180 lbs. per sq. in.

PACIFIC TYPE, FOUR-CYLINDER LOCOMOTIVE, LONDON, MIDLAND & SCOTTISH RAILWAY.

This 4-6-2 four-cylinder express locomotive, designed by Mr. W. A. Stainer, was built at Crewe Works in 1933 for the London, Midland & Scottish Railway, for working the Anglo-Scottish trains of 500 tons between Euston and Glasgow. It has a tractive power of no less than 40,300 lbs., the boiler having a fire grate area of 45 sq. ft., and a total heating surface, excluding superheater, of 2,713 sq. ft. The working pressure of the boiler is 250 lbs. per sq. in. The two inside cylinders drive the first pair of coupled wheels, while the outside drive the middle pair. The cylinders are each 16¼in. diameter by 28in. stroke, and the coupled wheels are 6ft. 6in. diameter. The weight of the engine loaded is 104½ tons, and of the tender, 54 tons 2 cwts. The overall length is 74ft. 4½in.

than that hitherto used with the idea of increasing the then average speed of 20 to 25 miles an hour, with loads of about 50 tons, and enabling the carriage bodies to be placed between the wheels which were to be larger than usual and so ensure easier riding and reduce resistance. By 1840 this latter idea was abandoned as inconvenient, the bodies being made wider and placed over the wheels.

A replica of the engine, using parts of the original, was made at Swindon Works for the railway centenary celebrations at Darlington in 1925, and afterwards exhibited at the " Fair of the Iron Horse," at Halethorpe, U.S.A., in 1927. It is now preserved at Swindon Works.

Some engines built for working mineral trains on the S. & D.R. as late as 1848 retained many features of Timothy Hackworth's designs. These were of the " Derwent " class, and had steeply inclined cylinders attached to the boiler at the back, the connecting rods driving the leading wheels. They had the combined flue and return multi-tubular boiler. Steam was taken from the dome through a large external elbow pipe to valve chests above the cylinders, and the exhaust pipe to the smoke-box was also outside. Two tenders were attached, one at each end, although one would have sufficed. The *Derwent* locomotive is still in existence, and may be seen at Bank Top Station, Darlington, together with *Locomotion* as mentioned previously.

The locomotive introduced by Edward Bury & Co., in 1832, is one of a type which was exclusively used on the London & Birmingham Railway, from 1837 to 1846. These engines had only four wheels and inside cylinders directly attached to inside bar framing. The feature of the boiler was the D-shaped fire-box, with its high-domed crown. These four-wheeled engines were found to oscillate considerably at high speeds. For goods traffic the wheels were coupled. One of these curious engines—No. 3 of the Furness Railway, best known as *Old Copper Nob* on account of its polished copper dome-shaped fire-box—is preserved at Barrow-in-Furness. It was built in 1846 by Bury and used for mineral traffic on the F.R. until 1898.

The *Rocket* and other locomotives of the 'thirties were four-wheeled engines, but in due course Stephenson's and other makers built six-wheeled engines, which became the general pattern for very many years. Large diameter, single driving-wheels, with inside cylinders, for high-speed service, and smaller diametered six-coupled wheels for freight and mineral service, came into general use.

In 1840 some American built "Norris" locomotives were imported for the Birmingham & Gloucester Railway; these were of the 4-2-0 type, with inclined cylinders, 4ft. driving wheels, and a leading bogie. They weighed 9.5 tons.

It has been generally supposed that these engines were employed exclusively on the Lickey incline, a very steep incline on this line with a grade of no less than 1 in 37, but they were used for ordinary passenger and goods traffic between Birmingham and Gloucester, the mail and express trains excepted. An extra engine of this type assisted trains up the Lickey incline.

The passenger engines of 1845, known as the "long boiler" type, had the driving axle in front of the fire-box, the outside cylinders being placed as far back as possible so as to reduce the weight on the front axle. Many of this type were built for British railways, and it became a standard on some of the French railways down to 1873.

Alexander Allan, manager of the Grand Junction Railway Works at Crewe, in 1841, introduced another notable class of passenger engine which had great influence on locomotive design for more than forty years. Owing to frequent breakages of crank axles of inside cylinder engines, Mr. Allan adopted straight axles with inclined outside cylinders. Similar engines were built at Crewe until 1858.

The G.W.R., completed between London and Bristol in 1841, was, as already stated, constructed on Brunel's 7ft. gauge. The broad-gauge line from London to Gloucester followed in 1845, and it was the

B

break of gauge at the latter place, where it met the standard gauge (4ft. 8½in.), from Birmingham, that led to the historic " battle of the gauges." The question of the comparative power, speed and safety of the locomotives used on the broad and narrow gauges, received so much attention that it was decided that a series of engine trials should be made. These were carried out in 1845-46 between a G.W.R. standard passenger engine for the broad gauge and one of Stephenson's long-boiler engines for the narrow. The experiments were inconclusive, but the Royal Commission appointed reported in favour of a standard 4ft. 8½in. gauge, which was subsequently fixed by legislation. Keen competition for speeds followed, with the result that some bold designs of locomotives were produced.

Francis Trevithick, son of Richard Trevithick, built a remarkable engine at Crewe, in 1847, for the L. & N.W.R. This was the famous *Cornwall*, with driving wheels 8ft. 6in. diameter. The outside cylinders were 17½in. diameter by 24in. stroke. The boiler was placed underneath the driving axle, and there were four carrying wheels at the front end, with two behind the fire-box. In 1858 the engine was rebuilt, with its boiler in the normal position ; it is still in existence.

Stephensons enlarged their long-boiler engine by adding a trailing axle behind the fire-box, and two were built for the L. & N.W.R. in 1848. They had 7ft. driving wheels, but the permanent way was too light and they were soon " scrapped."

The most celebrated of the broad-gauge engines was, probably, the *Lord of the Isles*, designed by Sir Daniel Gooch and built at Swindon in 1851, with 8ft. single driving wheels and cylinders 18in. diameter by 24in. stroke. Working pressure, 140 lbs. per sq. in. Tractive effort, 9,640 lbs. The tender was provided with a seat at the back facing the train, for the " travelling guard," whose duty it was to warn the driver if anything happened to the train.

From about 1850 the S. & D.R. adopted Stephenson's inside cylinder engines, with six-coupled wheels, in front of the fire-box.

On lines carrying coal traffic at low speeds, the long-boiler engine was found to be very handy when shunting into colliery sidings. One of these engines has been preserved at the York Museum.

In 1855 five 4-4-0 side tank engines were built by Stephenson & Co. for the North London Railway, and as regards wheel arrangements these were the forerunners of the later standard engines on this line.

The need for increased adhesion on heavily graded lines led to the adoption of four-coupled locomotives for passenger service, and the early 'sixties saw the introduction of the four-coupled bogie tender engine on the Great North of Scotland Railway.

John Ramsbottom, locomotive engineer of the L. & N.W.R., was responsible for the famous " Problem " class of six-wheeled single-wheelers, with 7ft. 6in. wheels, of 1860, of which the best known was the *Lady of the Lake* ; these engines lasted well into the twentieth century.

Among notable four-coupled passenger engines of the later 'sixties were Joseph Beattie's on the London & South Western Railway, with outside cylinders and fitted with his feed-water heating apparatus.

In 1870 Patrick Stirling built the first of his celebrated 8ft. single driving wheel express engines for the Great Northern Railway. They worked most of the main line services of that system until the end of the nineteenth century.

The " Precedent " class of four-coupled engines, of 1874, of the L. & N.W.R., had 6ft. 9in. driving wheels, familiarly known as the " Jumbos," the most celebrated of the series being the *Charles Dickens*, built in 1882. In just over twenty years this engine ran 2,000,000 miles, between Manchester and London, covering 367 miles daily for six days a week. There were 166 engines of this type. During the railway race to Scotland in 1895 the *Hardwicke* ran a racing train from Crewe to Carlisle, 141 miles, including Shap Summit, in 126 minutes at an average speed of 67.2 m.p.h. *Hardwicke* was withdrawn in 1932, and is preserved by the L.M. & S.R. as a locomotive of historic interest. Most of the " Jumbos " bore picturesque names : *Penrith Beacon, Raleigh, Merrie Carlisle, Luck of Edenhall, Skiddaw*, etc. *Snowdon*, the last to remain in service, was withdrawn in 1934 after nearly sixty years' work.

The much admired front-coupled engines of William Stroudley for the London, Brighton & South Coast Railway came out in 1882. Kept beautifully clean in their yellow livery, with copper capped chimneys, they were noted for reliability and punctual running. Probably the most famous of the class, *Gladstone*, has been preserved in its original condition at the Railway Museum, York. Many tank engines of this type are still doing useful work on the branch lines of the Southern Railway, after over fifty years of strenuous service.

The earliest passenger engines of the Highland Railway, dating from 1855, were six-wheeled, with 6ft. single driving wheels, with outside cylinders, and were virtually of the orthodox " Allan " type. Although single driver engines were obviously unsuited for such a mountainous line as that between Perth and Forres, some little locomotives of this type worked the passenger service in its early days.

Crampton engines of the " Folkestone " class ran for a time on the South Eastern and Great Northern Railways. The engines were carried on six wheels, and had outside cylinders, with valve chests on top. Express passenger engines of this type, patented by T. R. Crampton, in 1842-47, were built for the Eastern Railway of France in 1854, by Schneider & Co. The arrangement was adopted in order to keep the centre of gravity low and at the same time to use large single driving wheels which were carried on an axle behind the fire-box ; a number of these locomotives worked on express services until about 1878, and some lasted until quite recent years.

With the increase of traffic, as also the working of long gradients, the necessity of some form of power-operated brake became imperative. In the late 'seventies many systems were designed and experimented with, but two were finally adopted, namely, the air pressure and the vacuum. Both these brakes act not only on the engine and tender but also on the train, and were developed into automatic brakes, so arranged that in the event of the train breaking apart the brakes are automatically applied.

An important addition to the efficiency of the locomotive was affected by the introduction of injectors for feeding water into the boiler. In early engines this was performed by means of pumps operated by the engines while in motion, or, in some cases, by an auxiliary steam-operated pump. The injector has no moving parts, and depends entirely for its functioning on a small amount of the steam taken from the boiler.

The ten years between 1880 and 1890 brought locomotive engineering right up to what may be termed Modern Design, with the exception of superheating. During this period considerable attention was given to working locomotives on the compound expansion system, making more effective use of the steam generated in the boiler. In the normal locomotive the steam is admitted from the boiler direct to each cylinder on the simple expansion principle, the steam escaping direct from each cylinder into the atmosphere. In compound locomotives the cylinders are of unequal diameters, in which the steam from the boiler is used twice before being exhausted into the atmosphere.

On the L. & N.W.R. the "Webb" compound principle was adopted. The steam, after being used in two small cylinders, was exhausted into one very large one, of two to two and a half times the combined volumes of the high pressure ones, and there further expanded. One hundred express engines were built on this system, as well as many goods engines.

B2

CHAPTER II

PRESENT-DAY PASSENGER LOCOMOTIVES

D URING the past ten years or so radical changes have been introduced in the design of the steam locomotive, stimulated, no doubt, by the competition of electricity and oil engines. The adoption of higher working pressures seems to have opened up a new era not only in an increase in the tractive power, but in efficiency also. When George Stephenson built the *Rocket* a boiler pressure of 50 lbs. per sq. in. was employed, and pressures have gradually increased until now there are many engines running in this country working at 250 lbs. per sq. in.

The necessity for greater locomotive power steadily increased, and engines have grown to the maximum obtainable on the axle-loading permitted by the strength of the permanent way and bridges, yet traffic needs more power. In the latest types superheated steam is now universally used, considerably increasing the efficiency of the locomotive with economies in the consumption of fuel. Superheaters, as their name implies, are devices for adding heat to the steam after it is generated, not only to remove the moisture which ordinary saturated steam contains but of adding sufficient heat to prevent condensation taking place in the cylinders, where a portion of the energy is lost.

When increased train loads demanded larger boiler capacity for the locomotives and a wider fire-box, more weight had to be carried and more wheels were necessary, consequently as the grate could no longer be accommodated between the drivers a small pair of trailing wheels became indispensable.

This fact formed the basis of the design by H. A. Ivatt, locomotive engineer of the G.N.R., for the first *Atlantic* or 4-4-2 type express engine in this country—No. 990 (now No. 3990 of the London & North Eastern Railway).   The main characteristics are outside cylinders, two pairs of coupled wheels, with a four-wheeled bogie at the leading end and a pair of trailing wheels under the fire-box.

These engines were forerunners of the later *Atlantics* with larger and wider fire-box boilers with 31 sq. ft. grate area, the first of which, No. 251, left Doncaster Works in 1902.   For over twenty years they were the standard express engines of the G.N.R., and even now they are to be seen working some of the fastest trains on the L. & N.E. system, including the *Queen of Scots* Pullman and the Harrogate and West Riding expresses.

Recent passenger locomotives are for high speed express services, the speeding up of which reflect their efficiency.   We may take, as typical of these locomotives, the 4-6-0 *Royal Scot*, of the L.M. & S.R., 4-6-0 *King George V*, of the G.W., 4-6-0 *Lord Nelson*, of the Southern, and 4-6-2 *Flying Scotsman* of the L. & N.E.R.   The first named has three cylinders only, 18in. in diameter ; the second and third have four cylinders, 16¼in. and 16½in. diameter respectively, two outside and two inside, while the fourth has three cylinders, 20in. diameter.

These locomotives are fine specimens of design, and well up to their work with the heaviest trains.   If still more powerful engines are needed, it is due to the gradients which have to be climbed at some points.   The ideal engine is one that can take trains without help over these grades.

In 1927 the L.M. & S.R. decided to provide a more powerful locomotive for dealing with heavy through passenger trains by the West Coast route, between London and Edinburgh, 400 miles, and Glasgow, 401½ miles, and also for other main line sections of the system.   With this end in view, a three-cylinder simple-expansion superheated engine of the 4-6-0 type was designed of sufficient capacity. The inside cylinder drives on the crank axle of the leading pair of driving wheels and the two outside cylinders the middle pair.   The first of the series—No. 6100—was named *Royal Scot* and this title has been applied to the whole of the class. There are seventy of these engines in service ; the first fifty were built in 1927 by the North British Locomotive Co., and numbered 6100 to 6149 inclusive, a further series of twenty engines, numbered 6150 to 6169, built in the Company's workshops at Derby followed in 1930. These engines carry a working pressure of 250 lbs. per sq. in. The three cylinders are each 18in. diameter by 26in. stroke, and the coupled wheels are 6ft. 9in. diameter. The tractive effort is 33.150 lbs.

In order to permit locomotives to haul long distance non-stopping trains, water troughs are provided at intervals which vary from 25 to 60 miles apart. This arrangement enables water to be picked up without stopping by water scoop apparatus fitted on the tender and operated by hand-screw gear. By this means 1,500 gallons of water can be picked up in 20 seconds. These troughs have on the average a length of 440 yards, and are automatically refilled from tanks at the side of the line. This system of replenishing locomotives with feed-water was devised by the late John Ramsbottom, of the L. & N.W.R., back in the 'fifties.

The L.M. & S. main line between Lancaster and Carlisle, rising from sea-level to 915ft. up, at Shap Summit, is 32 miles, is a severe tax on locomotive capacity. When the load exceeds thirteen coaches the *Royal Scots* take an assistant engine over this gradient, which for four miles is at 1 in 75.

It will be remembered that the engine *Royal Scot* was shown at the Century of Progress Exhibition, Chicago, in 1933, after an exhibition tour of the principal cities of Canada and the United States. To conform to American requirements, the engine was fitted with a large electric headlight, as well as a warning bell, which is still carried on the front end. Some of these engines bear the names of famous regiments in the British Army, whilst others perpetuate the names of celebrated engines of the past.

The L.M. & S.R., in 1933, completed at Crewe Works the first two of a new class of passenger locomotives of the " Pacific " type—the *Princess Royal* (No. 6200), and *Princess Elizabeth* (No. 6201), designed by Mr. W. A. Stanier, chief mechanical engineer, for service on the heaviest expresses between London and Scotland. They are the most powerful passenger locomotives on the system, and share with the " King " class of the G.W.R. the distinction of being the most powerful six-coupled type (on a tractive effort basis) in the country.

Whereas the maximum load for the " Royal Scot " type, unassisted has been 420 tons, the new engines take trains up to 500 tons without assistance. The four cylinders are each $16\frac{1}{4}$in. diameter by 28in. stroke, and the coupled wheels 6ft. 6in. diameter. The boiler has a firegrate area of 45 sq. ft., and a total heating surface (excluding superheater) of 2,713 sq. ft. ; working pressure is 250 lbs. per sq. in. Development of the high tractive effort of 40,300 lbs. has been made possible by the employment, in conjunction with the large boiler, of the four-cylinder simple expansion arrangement, providing good balancing with a load of $22\frac{1}{2}$ tons on each of the driving axles. The tender—carried on three axles with roller-bearing journals—carries 4,000 gallons of water and 9 tons of coal. Total weight of engine and tender in working order is 158 tons 12 cwts., and the overall length is 74ft. $4\frac{1}{4}$in. These engines make the longest regular daily through locomotive journey, from London (Euston) to Glasgow (Central) and vice versa, $401\frac{1}{2}$ miles each day, climbing en route Shap and Beattock summits of 915ft. and 1,014ft. above sea-level, respectively.

The latest design of three-cylinder 4-6-0 express engine of the L.M. & S.R. (5 X class) has a tapered boiler barrel, with a working pressure of 225 lbs. per sq. in. The coupled wheels are 6ft. 9in. diameter, and the three cylinders are 17in. diameter by 26in. stroke, with separate sets of Walschaert valve gear. The boiler has an outside diameter of 5ft. increasing to 5ft. $8\frac{3}{8}$in., and is 13ft. 10in. in length. The feed water is supplied through valves provided on top of the boiler. The roomy cab has the driver's stand on the left-hand side, and is provided with tip-up seats. The tender carries 3,500 gallons of water and 7 tons of coal, although some have larger ones carrying 4,000 gallons of water and 9 tons of coal. Total weight of engine and tender, loaded, is 134 tons 17 cwts.

The first of the G.W. four-cylinder 4-6-0 express engines of the "Castle" class, the famous No. 4073, *Caerphilly Castle*, was built at Swindon in 1923, and shown at the British Empire Exhibition at Wembley of 1924. It is an enlargement of the earlier 4-6-0 express engines, with cylinders 16in. diameter by 26in. stroke. It has a tapered boiler 5ft. 9in. diameter at the fire-box end, with a length of 14ft. 10in. The coupled wheels are 6ft. 8½in. diameter. The total heating surface is 2,312 sq. ft., and the grate area 30.28 sq. ft. The working pressure is 225 lbs. per sq. in. The tractive effort is 31,625 lbs.

The "Castle" class proved very efficient, but a later and heavier design is the much admired "King" type, first built at Swindon Works in 1927, to the designs of Mr. C. B. Collett, chief mechanical engineer. The two inside cylinders drive on the inside cranks of the leading pair of wheels, and the outside pair are placed farther back and drive on the outside cranks of the second coupled axle. The four cylinders are each 16¼in. diameter by 28in. stroke ; the driving wheels are 6ft. 6in. diameter, and the tractive effort at 85% of the boiler pressure is 40,300 lbs. The boiler has a conical barrel 16ft. long and 6ft. maximum diameter ; the fire-box is of the Belpaire type, 11ft. 6in. long outside, with a grate area of 34.3 sq. ft. The heating surface is 2,514 sq. ft., and steam pressure 250 lbs. per sq. in. The weight on each pair of coupled wheels is 22½ tons, and the total weight 89 tons. The tender carries 4,000 gallons of water and 6 tons of coal. Total weight of engine and tender is 135.7 tons.

Designed to keep time with trains weighing up to 360 tons on the heavy inclines on the South Devon section of the main line, engines of both the " Castle " and " King " classes have gained an excellent reputation for efficiency in haulage, capacity and speed. One of the " Castle " class—No. 5006, *Tregenna Castle*—when hauling the *Cheltenham Flyer* covered the 77.3 miles from Swindon to Paddington in 56¾ minutes ; 39 miles of this were run at an average speed of about 90 m.p.h.

The first of the " King " class—No. 6000, *King George V*—was sent to the United States to take part in the Baltimore and Ohio Railroad Centenary celebrations, in 1927, and as a memento of the visit was presented with a large brass bell, similar to those carried on American locomotives, and this is still on the front buffer beam.

The well-known " Lord Nelson " class engines of the S.R. will haul trains of 500 tons at an average speed of 55 miles an hour over any section of the main lines. The four cylinders are all 16½in. diameter by 26in. stroke, placed in line, the inside pair driving the first coupled axle and the outside pair the second axle ; each is actuated by separate Walschaert valve gear. A peculiar feature of these engines is that, in order to avoid a dead centre, the four cranks are set at an angle of 135° to each other. This means that four exhaust beats occur with every revolution of the wheels. It is usual in four-cylinder engines to simply duplicate the two-cylinder arrangement by setting all four cranks at 90° to each other, but this still means only four efforts—or exhaust beats—for each revolution, as in the two-cylinder type. In the " Lord Nelson " class the cranks are so spaced that eight efforts, or exhaust beats, are obtained per revolution, which means more even turning effort. In other words, double the number—but smaller—efforts are made during one revolution, and thus the stresses are not only lower but more equalized, through each turn of the driving wheels, and, consequently, there is less wear and tear throughout ; also there is the advantage of more even draught upon the fire, and conducive to better combustion. The coupled wheels are 6ft. 7in. diameter, with a wheelbase of 17ft., and the tractive effort is 33,510 lbs. The boiler has a Belpaire fire-box ; its total heating surface is 2,365 sq. ft., and the grate area is 33 sq. ft. The working pressure is 220 lbs. per sq. in.

There are sixteen of these engines in service between London (Victoria) and Dover, and on the Bournemouth and Salisbury services from Waterloo.

The bulk of the express services on the Dover, Bournemouth and Exeter main lines of the S.R. is worked by the " King Arthur " class of 4-6-0 two-cylinder express locomotives, brought out in 1925. They are named after the " Knights of the Round Table," and other characters mentioned in the Arthurian legend.

Until the " Nelson " class was introduced in 1926 they were the most powerful passenger engines on the Southern. They have 20½in. by 26in. cylinders, and 200 lbs. per sq. in. boiler pressure. To conform to the smaller loading gauge of the Eastern section, modifications have been made in the shape of the driver's cab, etc.

A number of really powerful locomotives of the 4-4-0 type, with three cylinders, have been built since 1930 at the Eastleigh Works of the S.R., for the main line routes to the Kentish coast resorts, as well as to Portsmouth, where severe gradients and increasing weight of modern rolling stock require their use. The restricted construction gauge of the Hastings line necessitate them being as small and compact as possible. These engines are named after famous public schools, hence they are known as the " Schools " class.

Although not nearly as large and heavy as the " Lord Nelson " and " King Arthur " classes, these engines rank as the most powerful four-coupled type in the country. Due to load limitations on the axles a round-topped fire-box was adopted instead of the Belpaire pattern ; this, however, permits a better outlook for the driver. The three cylinders are each 16½in. diameter by 26in. stroke, and the driving wheels 6ft. 7in. diameter, spaced 10ft. centre to centre. The piston valves are driven by three separate sets of Walschaert valve gear. At 85% of the boiler pressure of 220 lbs. per sq. in., the tractive effort is 25,130 lbs. The boiler barrel is 5ft. 5¾in. diameter and 11ft. 9in. long ; its heating surface is 1,766 sq. ft., and grate area 28.3 sq. ft. The superheater surface is 283 sq. ft. The engine weighs 67.1 tons, of which 42 tons rest on the coupled wheels. The tender carries 4,000 gallons of water and 5 tons of coal.

Between 1914 and 1922, seven large 4-6-4 type tank locomotives were built by the L.B. & S.C.R. at Brighton Works. These conformed to the construction gauge of the L.B. & S.C.R., which is larger than of other lines forming part of the S.R., and so confined their use to the Brighton section. In view of the electrification of the lines from London to Brighton, and Eastbourne, these engines were no longer required for the work for which they were designed. They have, therefore, been converted to 4-6-0 type tender engines at Eastleigh Works. The first one dealt with is engine No. 2329, which bears the name *Stephenson*. The numbers and names allotted to the other six are : 2327, *Trevithick*, 2328 *Hackworth*, 2330 *Cudworth*, 2331 *Beattie*, 2332 *Stroudley*, and 2333 *Remembrance*. A new cab with side windows has been fitted and also a shorter chimney, enabling the engines to be used on almost any of the Southern main lines. The main particulars are : cylinders, 22in. diameter by 28in. stroke ; coupled wheels, 6ft. 9in. diameter ; boiler heating surface, evaporative 1,816 sq. ft. ; superheater, 838 sq. ft. Total 2,199 sq. ft. Grate area, 26.6 sq. ft. Weight of engine in working order, 73 tons 9 cwts. The bogie tender carries 5,000 gallons of water, with a coal capacity of 5 tons. Tractive effort is estimated at 25,600 lbs. Working pressure has been increased to 180 lbs. per sq. in.

The " Pacific," or 4-6-2 type engines of the L. & N.E.R., introduced in 1922, work the express trains by the East Coast route to Scotland, and during the summer cover the 392¾ miles between London and Edinburgh without stop.

There are now seventy-eight of these engines in service ; all but six bear names after famous race-horses, the majority of which have won the Derby or St. Leger. The striking features are the large boiler and fire-box, in particular. The grate is wider than it is long, with an area of $41\frac{1}{4}$ sq. ft. Further, the inner fire-box projects forward into the boiler barrel, thus shortening the length between tubeplates ; the result is a fire-box with a heating surface of 215 sq. ft. The boiler barrel is 5ft. 9in. diameter outside, at its least, and 6ft. 5in. at its largest diameter. Working pressure is 180 lbs. per sq. in. The heating surface is 3,455 sq. ft., of which the superheater contributes 525 sq. ft. Later engines of this type have been built with boilers carrying 220 lbs. per sq. in. pressure. The engines detailed to work the non-stop " Flying Scotsman " trains are provided with special corridor tenders to enable the driver and fireman to be changed en route. This tender runs on eight wheels, and carries 5,000 gallons of water and 9 tons of coal. The total weight of engine and tender is 154 tons. These engines have 6ft. 8in. driving wheels, and three cylinders, 20in. diameter by 26in. stroke.

A good method of testing the power of an engine is to work it on a road for which it had not been specially built, thus the L. & N.E. and G.W.R., in 1925, exchanged locomotives for awhile. The G.W.R. *Pendennis Castle* ran the " Flying Scotsman " between King's Cross and York ; and *Victor Wild*, of the L. & N.E.R., the " Cornish Riviera " to Plymouth and back. Both engines proved themselves able to deal efficiently with the trains, and, although the G.W. engine was lighter and burned less coal, general results were not decisive.

Mention should be made of a remarkable test run made on November 30th, 1934, from King's Cross to Leeds and back, with Pacific engine No. 4472, *Flying Scotsman*, with a train of four vehicles, or about 145 tons. It left King's Cross at 9.8 a.m. and arrived at Leeds (Central) 2 hrs. 32 mins. later, thus achieving an average speed of 73.4 m.p.h. for the $185\frac{3}{4}$ miles. On one stretch of 25 miles an average of $90\frac{1}{2}$ m.p.h. was maintained. The return journey, with six coaches attached, took 2 hrs. 37 mins., or 5 minutes longer. Near Little Bytham a speed of 100 m.p.h. was attained. The gradients run to 1 in 200 between London and Doncaster, and 1 in 100 thence to Leeds.

The L. & N.E.R. beat the world's record for speed made by a steam train by running from London to Newcastle-on-Tyne under four hours on March 5th, 1935, the distance being 268 miles. The train was hauled by Pacific type engine No. 2750, *Papyrus*, built in 1929, and comprised a dynamometer car, restaurant car, three first-class corridor coaches, and brake van—a weight of 213 tons.

The train left King's Cross at 9.8 a.m. and reached Newcastle at $1.4\frac{1}{2}$ p.m., nearly 4 minutes ahead of schedule. As far as Doncaster, timings were inside schedule, but owing to a derailment of some wagons at Arksey, it was necessary to slow down and finally stop, because of single line working ahead. In consequence, the train was a minute behind time passing York (188 miles) in $2\frac{1}{4}$ hours, but at Darlington the lost time had been regained ; the average speed for the whole journey was $67\frac{1}{2}$ m.p.h., or $68\frac{1}{2}$ if 4 minutes is allowed for the Doncaster delay. The highest speed recorded was 88 m.p.h.

At Gateshead sheds *Papyrus* was found to be in excellent condition and at 3.47 p.m. the return journey was begun. As far as Grantham schedule times only were kept, as a long slack was necessary north of Doncaster, at the scene of the derailed coal train, but after this driver Sparshatt took the opportunity of showing what his engine could do. For twelve miles from Corby and down the long drop from Stoke signal box to Tallington, the average speed was over 100 m.p.h., whilst just south of Little Bytham 105.5 m.p.h. was registered for 30 seconds, and for 10 seconds it reached 108 m.p.h.

The whole journey from Newcastle to King's Cross was completed in 3 hrs. 51 mins. at an average speed of 69.6 miles an hour. The train had thus covered 536.4 miles in 7 hrs. $47\frac{1}{2}$ mins.

THE " TORBAY LIMITED " EXPRESS, GREAT WESTERN RAILWAY, PASSING TWYFORD.
    (Photo : A. P. Reavil.)

At 12 o'clock noon, the down " Torbay Limited," one of the principal trains of the Great Western Railway, leaves Paddington on its run of 199¾ miles to Torquay, where it is due at 3.35 p.m., maintaining an average speed of 56.2 miles per hour. It is worked by locomotives of the " Castle " or " King " class, and frequently comprises fourteen coaches, weighing well over 500 tons. The running between Paddington and Exeter, 179¾ miles in 169 minutes, averages 61.6 m.p.h.

There are very few gradients worth mentioning on the run of the " Torbay Limited," as from London to Reading it is nearly dead level, and thence onward there are few trying grades other than the stiff climb from Taunton up to Whiteball summit, so that this train is much easier to work than the famous 10.30 " Cornish Riviera Ltd.," which has some terribly hard climbs beyond Newton Abbot, with the load cut down to eight coaches, or 300 tons.

THE " GOLDEN ARROW, PULLMAN, LIMITED," SOUTHERN RAILWAY. *(Photo : H. G. Tidey.)*

From Victoria Station, London, to Dover Marine Station, the distance is 78 miles, and the time scheduled 93 minutes, does not appear particularly remarkable, but a congested and exacting road are reasons why the running is not accelerated. The " Golden Arrow " is the British portion of the Paris and London service of that name, and, when started a few years back, was made up of Pullman cars only, but owing to the falling off in Continental traffic now consists of four or five Pullmans included in the ordinary 11 o'clock boat train, usually worked by a " Lord Nelson " or " King Arthur " class engine.

" ROYAL SCOT " TRAIN, LONDON, MIDLAND & SCOTTISH RAILWAY. *(Photo : H. G. Tidey.)*

These expresses, which leave London and Scotland simultaneously at 10 a.m. every week-day, are made up of fifteen corridor carriages of the most modern design, weighing about 417 tons, empty. Of these, nine work between London and Glasgow (Central), and six to and from Edinburgh (Princes Street). Running non-stop during the summer season from Euston to Kingmoor (just north of Carlisle), 300 miles, engines are changed here, and then a second stop is made at Symington to divide the train. The 401½ miles between London and Glasgow are covered in 7 hrs. 40 mins., or at the rate of 52.4 miles per hour. In the return direction the Glasgow and Edinburgh portions are combined at Symington, and the next stop is at Carlisle (No. 12 signal box). The up train is due at Euston at 5.40 p.m.

When the train is run in two sections, the Symington stop is often omitted.

THE " FLYING SCOTSMAN," LONDON & NORTH EASTERN RAILWAY. (*Photo : H. G. Tidey.*)

Usually this famous train is made up of nine 60ft. cars, together with a triplet restaurant car set, representing a load of 550 tons out of London, when, in the summer, it makes its non-stop run between the capital cities of England and Scotland, 392¾ miles, both north and south in 7½ hours ; the average speed is 52.4 miles per hour throughout.

Corridor tenders are provided, so that a relief crew is carried, and a change-over made half-way. The tender carries 5,000 gallons of water, and picks up as much again from the six water troughs laid down on the way.

The equipment of the train includes a Louis XVI restaurant car, electric kitchen, ladies' retiring room, hair-dressing saloon, and Vita-glass windows.

THE " WEST RIDING PULLMAN " EXPRESS, NEAR POTTERS BAR, LONDON & NORTH EASTERN RAILWAY. (*Photo : E. R. Wethersett.*)

Made up of seven or eight Pullman cars, weighing between 300 and 340 tons, the " West Riding Pullman " is made up of two portions—King's Cross and Halifax (202¾ miles), and King's Cross and Newcastle, via Harrogate (280¾ miles), dividing at Wakefield. It leaves King's Cross at 4.45 p.m. every week-day and, after making four stops, completes the journey to Halifax in 4 hrs. 12 mins., and to Newcastle in 5 hrs. 38 mins.

On Sundays its place is taken by the " Harrogate Sunday Pullman," non-stop to Leeds, where division takes place so as to serve Harrogate and Bradford.

These trains are amongst the fastest on the London & North Eastern Railway system, and are usually worked by the very efficient " Atlantic " type engines of the erstwhile Great Northern Railway.

THE " IRISH MAIL " PASSING CONWAY, LONDON, MIDLAND & SCOTTISH RAILWAY.

Between Euston and Holyhead—263¾ miles—there are two " Irish Mail " trains each way on week days, for the steamers to Kingstown, for Dublin. The trains are usually worked by 4-6-0, three-cylinder engines of the rebuilt " Baby Scot " class, with 6ft. 9in. drivers, which work at the high pressure of 200 lbs. per sq. inch. The cylinders are 18in. dia.×26in. stroke.

After mounting the incline from Euston to Camden, the grading of the line all the way to Holyhead is particularly good and the running easy, so that in spite of the heavy loads, remarkably good time-keeping is the rule.

En route from Chester, the Conway river and the Menai Straits are crossed by iron, tubular bridges. The latter, Robert Stephenson's famous Britannia Bridge, is carried on three towers, the centre one built on the Britannia rock, and 230ft. in height. The two main spans are no less than 460ft. long, while the distance above water level is more than 100ft.

The illustration shows the day " Irish Mail " passing the picturesque ruins of Conway Castle.

C

The latest design of express engine of the L. & N.E.R. is to deal with the problem of working single-headed, trains up to 550 tons over the Edinburgh-Aberdeen section, which abounds in heavy grades and several speed restrictions, and needs spurts of high-speed to maintain the running schedules. The 2-8-2 wheel arrangement has been adopted by Mr. Gresley, so that the wheelbase has not been unduly protracted, being only 2ft. 2in. in excess of the Pacifics. The apparent streamlining effect is introduced mainly to raise the exhaust steam and smoke clear of the driver's cab. The side sheets form a complete covering, right up to the limits of the construction gauge of the projections on the boiler barrel, and so prevent smoke eddies forming. The long-shaped dome is covered, and acts as a steam collector, communicating with the boiler by a number of slots ; it also houses the regulator. The grate area is 50 sq. ft., and this is the largest yet provided on a British express locomotive. By using eight-coupled driving wheels, a total adhesion of 80 tons 12 cwts. is obtained without unduly loading individual axles. In working order the total weight of the engine is 110 tons 5 cwts. Three cylinders, 21in. in diameter and 26in. stroke, drive on to coupled wheels, 6ft. 2in. diameter. With a boiler working pressure of 220 lbs. per sq. in., the engine develops a tractive effort of 43,462 lbs.

The first of the class—No. 2001, *Cock o' the North*—has cam-operated poppet valves and gear, while the second, No. 2002, *Earl Marischal*, has piston valves and Walschaert motion. The tender, which accommodates 8 tons of coal and 5,000 gallons of water, and is carried on eight wheels, weighs in working order 55 tons 6 cwts., so that the total weight of the engine and tender together amounts to 165 tons 11 cwts.

To deal with the traffic requirements of East Anglia, a special design of three-cylinder 4-6-0 engine was introduced by Mr. Gresley in 1928. For its size and weight it is a powerful machine, and well suited for the heavy gradients met with on the Great Eastern section.

By permission of H.M. the King, the first of the series, No. 2800, is named *Sandringham*. The remainder bear names of country seats, except No. 2845, which is named the *Suffolk Regiment*.

The diameter of 17½in. and the piston stroke of 26in. is common to all cylinders. The drive is divided, the inside cylinder acting upon the leading coupled axle, and the external pair upon the middle coupled wheels. The boiler barrel is in two rings of 5ft. 6in. and 5ft. 4½in. diameter, with a length of 13ft. 6in. The boiler pressure is 200 lbs. per sq. in., and the tractive effort is 25,380 lbs.

For lighter main line and cross-country services, particularly in the north-east of England and Scotland, Mr. Gresley introduced in 1927 a class of powerful three-cylinder 4-4-0 express locomotives. Twenty-eight of these symmetrical looking engines were built at Darlington during 1927-28, and another eight in 1929, and named after the " Shires." A further series of forty have been named after famous " Hunts " in the districts served by the L. & N.E.R., whilst two of the original set have been renamed after " Hunts."

The three-cylinders are in one casting, and are 17in. diameter, with a stroke of 26in. Piston valves, 8in. diameter, with a maximum travel of 6in., are actuated by Walschaert motion for the outside cylinders, and by Gresley gear for the inside valve, the levers for driving the latter being arranged behind the cylinders and operated by the outside motion. Six of the " Shire " series, and the whole of the " Hunt " class, have cylinders served by poppet valves. The six " Shire " class engines have poppet valves operated by Walschaert gear and oscillating cams ; the " Hunt " class have poppet valves operated by rotary cams. They have coupled wheels, 6ft. 8in. diameter, carry a working pressure of 180 lbs. per sq. in., and have a heating surface of 1669.58 sq. ft., and grate area of 26 sq. ft.

CHAPTER III

MODERN MIXED TRAFFIC, GOODS AND TANK ENGINES

TWO main considerations have governed the locomotive construction policy of the British railways during recent years ; first, reliability, in order to obtain by more intensive use a greater revenue-earning mileage, and secondly, the development of a locomotive which can appropriately handle both passenger and freight trains.

Mixed traffic engines, as they are termed, are generally of the 2-6-0 type and, although they rarely have large driving wheels, can travel at fairly high speeds. The majority have outside cylinders, whilst a number on the L. & N.E. and S. Rys. are of the three-cylinder type. Until recently the standard, L.M. & S. mixed traffic engines, introduced in 1926, had the cylinders slightly inclined, which enabled them to be set higher than the cranks, to clear station platforms, which they slightly overlap. The later designs, with a higher pressure of 200 lbs. per sq. in., have horizontal cylinders of smaller bore but providing a similar tractive effort.

The first 2-6-0 engines of a definite mixed traffic character appeared on the Great Western in 1910. Coupled wheels of 5ft. 8in. diameter enable a good speed to be obtained on passenger services, and sufficient power to be developed to work fairly heavy goods trains.

Another numerous class of Great Western engine of the 4-6-0 two-cylinder type with 6ft. wheels, introduced in 1928, has proved very efficient for hauling excursion trains, as well as fast freight ; these bear names of famous " Halls " on the Great Western line. They have 18½in. by 30in. outside cylinders, and carry a working pressure of 225 lbs. per sq. in. ; the tractive effort is 27,275 lbs. The boiler is of the taper pattern, with Belpaire fire-box and top-feed. Audible signalling apparatus is fitted in the cab for use with the automatic train stop installation, with which the Great Western main lines are now equipped. Other particulars are : total heating surface, 2,104 sq. ft. ; grate area, 27.07 sq. ft. The engine in working order weighs 75 tons, and the tender, when loaded with 3,500 gallons of water and 6 tons of coal, 40 tons.

Mention should also be made of the " 4700 " class of Great Western 2-8-o's. These engines are exceptional, as they are the only ones in this country with coupled wheels of a diameter of 5ft. 8in.

A numerous and very efficient class of 2-6-o mixed traffic engine is adopted by the S.R. for fast goods trains to and from Southampton and the West of England, and on the Eastern section also, as well as for excursion traffic when required ; on the heavily-graded lines west of Exeter they are used for all classes of traffic. These have driving wheels, 5ft. 6in. diameter and cylinders 19in. by 28in. They carry a working pressure of 200 lbs. per sq. in.

For heavy goods trains hauled at moderate speeds, small wheels are better adapted to the class of traffic. By coupling the wheels with side rods the power exerted by the cylinders is communicated to all the wheels at once ; the larger the number of coupled wheels the better the adhesion which the engine gets on the rail. To provide sufficient tractive effort, a boiler that will generate enough steam must be provided, and, to spread the weight over a fair length of line, the engine must be sufficiently long.

Until recent years the standard freight and shunting engine design of the British railways has been the six-coupled or o-6-o type, and as a proof of their general utility are still being constructed as a general standard for the L. & N.E. and G.W. Rys. The latest examples on the former and used for mineral traffic in the Fife and Edinburgh districts are of the " J 38 " class, which have coupled wheels, 4ft. 8in. diameter, and cylinders 20in. diameter by 26in. stroke. Another o-6-o class, the " J 39," with larger wheels, 5ft. 2in. diameter have proved most useful with fast goods or excursion traffic.

C2

The G.W.R., in 1930, built twenty 0-6-0 engines for light main line traffic and branch line services. These engines have taper boilers and large cabs, with side windows and up-to-date equipment, including audible cab signalling apparatus. They have inside cylinders, 17½in by 24in.; coupled wheels, 5ft. 2in. diameter, and work at a pressure of 200 lbs. per sq. in. The tractive effort is 20,155 lbs.

A large number of 0-6-0 superheater goods engines were built from 1911 onwards for the Midland Railway, and its successors, the L.M. & S.R., to the designs of Sir Henry Fowler, then chief mechanical engineer. They have two inside cylinders, 20in. diameter by 26in. stroke, with six-coupled driving wheels, 5ft. 3in. diameter, on a wheelbase of 16ft. 6in. The tractive effort at 85% of the boiler pressure is 24,555 lbs. The boiler has a total heating surface of 1,410 sq. ft., and a grate area of 21.1 sq. ft., the steam pressure being 175 lbs. per sq. in.

The L.M. & S.R. have thirty-three Beyer-Garratt articulated locomotives of the 2-6-0 + 0-6-2 type, for hauling coal trains between Toton, in Derbyshire, and Brent sidings, near London, a distance of 126 miles on a schedule of under 8 hours. These are powerful machines, with a light axle loading, thus obviating strengthening many of the bridges on the Midland division. Each engine has four cylinders, 18½in. diameter by 26in. stroke, with driving wheels, 5ft. 3in. diameter. The steam pressure is 190 lbs. per sq. in., and the tractive effort 45,620 lbs.

Each of the L.M. & S.R. Beyer-Garratts replaces two ordinary locomotives while hauling trains of about 1,400 tons weight, or 90 loaded wagons. On the return journey they take 100 empty wagons (train limited in length). These engines have an overall length of 87ft. 10½in., and weigh 145 tons 14 cwts. A curious arrangement of barrel-shaped coal bunker is provided on these engines. The coal is put into a large cylinder, which slopes slightly towards the foot-plate. By turning a handle in the cab the bunker starts to revolve, bringing down the coal to the front, where the fireman can easily deal with it with his shovel—this tends to lighten his labour ; the turning is effected by a small steam engine. Being covered in, no coal dust from the bunker is blown into the cab when the engine is running bunker first.

For ordinary goods and the mineral traffic from South Wales, " Consolidation," or 2-8-0 type locomotives are preferred by the Great Western, and for the Derby and Nottingham coal trains to London by the L. & N.E.R., whilst the L.M. & S.R. are also using some of this type.

The Great Western 2-8-0 engines were put into service in 1903, and were the first of the type in this country. They have 4ft. 7½in. diameter wheels ; outside cylinders, 18½in. by 30in. and taper boilers. They work at 200 lbs. pressure, and have 2,143 sq. ft. of heating surface. Later ones have 225 lbs. pressure. The latest L. & N.E.R. Consolidations have three high pressure cylinders, all 18½in. by 26in. stroke ; 4ft. 8in. diameter coupled wheels ; and boilers 5ft. 6in. diameter, and on the main line are rated to haul 80 wagons of coal (1,300 tons) from Peterborough to London. The L.M. & S.R. has a large number of 0-8-0 type engines, as also has the L. & N.E.R. The L.M. & S. engines have inside cylinders, 19in. by 26in., and coupled wheels, 4ft. 8½in. diameter. Boiler pressure 200 lbs. per sq. in. Tractive force, 28,250 lbs.

Designed to haul mineral trains of 100 loaded wagons, or 1,600 tons, on the Great Northern main line, two engines of the " Mikado," or 2-8-2 type, Nos. 2393-4, built at Doncaster in 1925, were the first of the type in the British Isles. Further, they were each fitted with an auxiliary " booster " engine, working on the trailing wheels, to assist the locomotive when starting, or ascending the heavier gradients. These locomotives have three cylinders, 20in. by 26in. stroke. The coupled wheels are 5ft. 2in. diameter, or 6in. larger than the 2-8-0 engine of 1921, and a higher speed can be attained. The " booster " has two cylinders, 10in. diameter with a stroke of 12in., providing an additional tractive effort of 8,500 lbs. and making the maximum tractive effort of the engine 47,000 lbs. The weight of the engine and tender just exceeds 151 tons.

In 1919 Sir Henry Fowler designed for the L.M. & S.R., for assisting trains up the Lickey Incline, between Cheltenham and Birmingham, two miles at 1 in 37, a large ten-coupled tender engine, with four cylinders 16¾in. diameter by 28in. stroke, and 4ft. 7⅛in. wheels. Two piston valves only are provided, operated by Walschaert valve gear. This engine weights 73¾ tons, and is the only ten-coupled engine in Great Britain. Previously two 0-6-0 tank engines had to be used together for the banking of heavy trains, but " No. 2290 " does the work alone. The incline mentioned is the steepest on any main line in the country, and the engine spends all its working life running up and down this two-mile stretch. A large electric headlight is used for " spotting " the train to be banked up when coming on behind, as the engine is not actually coupled to the train and just slacks off at the summit.

Tank locomotives are often employed on fast passenger as well as goods trains, even for fairly long distances.

On the G.W.R. the 2-6-2 arrangement was introduced in 1903. This engine had 5ft. 8in. wheels, outside cylinders 18in. by 30in., taper boiler, and tanks holding 1,380 gallons of water. A later series had larger boilers and 2,000 gallon tanks. More recently they have all been fitted with superheaters. Many are used for assisting trains through the Severn tunnel. A later class—" 4500 "—first built in 1906, have 4ft. 7½in. wheels, outside cylinders 17in. by 24in., and tanks carrying 1,000 gallons of water. A similar, but still lighter, class for certain small branches have 4ft. 1½in. wheels and 17in. by 24in. cylinders.

For the L. & N.E.R. fast suburban traffic in the Edinburgh and Newcastle areas and the services from Glasgow in connection with the Clyde and Loch Lomond steamers a handsome tank engine of similar type but with three cylinders was designed by Mr. H. N. Gresley, chief mechanical engineer, and built at Doncaster in 1930 and later.

The cylinders are each 16in. diameter by 26in. stroke, driving the second pair of coupled wheels. Steam distribution is effected by Walschaert gear to the outside valves and by the Gresley gear, operated by extensions to the front of the outside valve spindles for the inside valve. The coupled wheels are 5ft. 8in. diameter. The boiler, with a working pressure of 180 lbs. per sq. in., is 5ft. diameter and 12ft. 2in. long.

The Great Western put into service in 1910 a 2-8-0 tank engine, known as the " 5200 " class, for dealing with the coal traffic in South Wales from the pits to the port of shipment. Owing to the falling off in the export trade they were not required for this service, and have been converted at Swindon to the 2-8-2 type, having larger coal and water capacity to make them suitable for main line mineral service. They have two cylinders, 19in. diameter by 30in. stroke ; driving wheels, 4ft. 7½in. diameter ; boiler pressure 200 lbs. per sq. in. Tractive effort, 33,170 lbs. Water capacity of tanks, 2,500 gallons. Weight in working order, 92 tons 12 cwts.

An example of the efforts made to improve the working conditions afforded enginemen will be appreciated by comparing some of the old engines referred to earlier in this book and the modern 2-6-4 type tank engines for fast suburban services of the L.M. & S.R. A closed-in cab, with let-down windows, is provided, while the sides of the coal bunker have been " flared " to give perfect visibility when running bunker first. There is also a " sunshine roof," or sliding panel, in the roof of the cab, for extra ventilation in hot weather. This engine has two cylinders, 19in diameter by 26in stroke ; driving wheels, 5ft. 9in. diameter ; boiler pressure, 200 lbs. per sq. in. ; tractive effort, 24,600 lbs.

CHAPTER IV

SOME UNUSUAL TYPES OF STEAM LOCOMOTIVES

CONVENTIONAL designs of steam locomotives are usually described by a distinctive name, such as " Mogul," " Consolidation," " Mikado," " Atlantic," " Mountain," " Pacific," etc. The distinctive name is generally followed by figures, which denote the arrangement of the wheels by what is known as the " Whyte " numerical system of classification. Commencing at the front, the wheels are divided into three groups : leading bogie, or pony truck ; driving wheels, and trailing truck, or bogie, wheels. Thus the numerical classification of a " Mogul " locomotive is 2-6-0, indicating a two-wheeled pony truck, six-coupled driving wheels and no trailing wheels. A " Mikado " 2-8-2 signifies a two-wheeled bogie truck, eight driving wheels and a two-wheeled trailing truck, and so on.

There have been many ingenious efforts to depart from traditional designs in a desire to effectively deal with the conditions.

Gear-driven locomotives built by the Sentinel Waggon Works for pick-up goods trains and shunting duties, have unusual features. A vertical boiler carrying a high working pressure, mostly 275 to 300 lbs. per sq. in., supplies steam to one or more high-speed steam engines with vertical cylinders and poppet valves. The engines drive a jack-shaft through gearing, and from there one pair of wheels is driven by a pair of chains, whilst the two pairs of wheels are coupled by a pair of chains instead of by side coupling rods.

A novel development of this principle is embodied in some gear-driven locomotives for a metre gauge railway in Colombia, with steep gradients. The main frame carrying the boiler, tanks, bunker, cab, etc., is mounted on two six-wheeled bogies. Each of the six axles is separately driven through gearing by a small steam engine mounted on the bogie. Separate flexible steam pipes with ball joints connect each engine with a main throttle valve, and allow for movements of the engine. Each engine is a double-acting compound with cylinders 4¼in. and 7¼in. diameter by 6in. stroke, driving a crank shaft carrying at its centre a pinion which meshes with a gear wheel on the centre of the corresponding axle ; the ratio is 2.74 : 1.

As steam is generated in a water tube boiler at the high working pressure of 550 lbs. per sq. in., ingenious arrangements are made to reduce this to 140 lbs. before it is admitted to the low-pressure cylinders when starting up. Steam is taken to each engine from a main throttle, and to ensure individual control the poppet valve regulator closes on to a conical seat and has a piston connection with six ports, each admitting steam to one engine. The tractive effort is estimated at 17,500 lbs. ; as all axles are driven, a maximum adhesive weight is assured.

Among notable high-pressure locomotives which have been produced in recent years, the Delaware & Hudson Railroad had one built in 1924 with a pressure of 350 lbs. per sq. in. This engine, named *Horatio Allen*, is a two-cylinder compound with a 2-8-0 wheel arrangement, the tender being fitted with a booster. The boiler followed usual practice, but over it, on each side, two cylindrical drums are fixed. Two shorter drums form the lower sides of the fire-box, the front wall being formed by a flat water space with ordinary stays. The upper drums are connected to this water space, and pass through it. The boiler barrel is secured to the front wall of the water space ; the rear plate of the water space is cut away for the fire-box tube-plate which is fixed in it, and the drums are attached to it. The back end of the fire-box is formed by a similar flat water space into which the rear ends of the four drums are secured. The top of the fire-box between the upper drums is formed by water tubes connecting the front and back water spaces, and each of the sides by two rows of curved water tubes joining the upper and lower drums. The front ends of the upper drums are connected to the boiler barrel by headers. With this boiler about one-third of the evaporative heating surface is in the fire-box, whereas in ordinary locomotive boilers the fire-box surface is only about one-tenth of the total.

A similar engine was obtained in 1927 which was called *John B. Jervis*. The pressure was raised to 400 lbs. per sq. in., and a greater superheating surface given. This was followed in 1930 by another 2-8-0 compound fitted with a water-tube boiler of the same general design, with a pressure of 500 lbs. per sq. in., and this was named *James Archibald*.

Following these experimental locomotives, all of which have shown exceptional thermal efficiency, the Delaware & Hudson Co. showed at the Chicago Exhibition of 1934 a 4-8-0 four-cylinder triple expansion locomotive, No. 1403, *L. F. Loree*, which carries a boiler pressure of 500 lbs. per sq. in. This is the second application of the triple expansion principle to a steam locomotive, the first being the somewhat abortive experiments carried out on the L. & N.W.R. in 1895. This engine of the D. & H.R.R. has one high-pressure cylinder, 20in. diameter by 32in. stroke, located under the driver's side of the cab, one intermediate pressure $27\frac{1}{2}$in. diameter by 32in. stroke under the fireman's side, and two low pressure 33in. by 32in. in the orthodox position, under the smoke-box. All four cylinders drive on the second pair of coupled wheels. Steam is distributed by poppet valves to all cylinders. The boiler has a water tube fire-box and a fire-tube barrel of relatively small diameter and completely filled with water. The steam space is in the drums of the fire-box, which are carried forward beyond the fire-box and connected to the barrel near the front ends. In starting steam is fed to the intermediate cylinder receiver direct from the high-pressure steam chest through a spring loaded feed valve, which closes when a pressure of 170 lbs. is reached in the receiver.

The coupled wheels are 5ft. 3in. diameter. The tender has one four- and one six-wheeled bogie, the latter being fitted with an auxiliary booster engine, taking steam direct from the boiler at 500 lbs. pressure. At starting, in simple gear, the tractive effort is estimated at 90,000 lbs., and when working triple expansion 75,000 lbs. When the booster is working at starting, an additional tractive power of 18,000 lbs. is developed.

In the experimental four-cylinder compound locomotive No. 10,000 of the L. & N.E.R., built in 1929, it was decided to use a working pressure of 450 lbs. per sq. in., and adopt a Yarrow-Gresley water-tube boiler. As its name implies, the water-tube boiler consists of a number of tubes which carry the water, and which are surrounded by the hot gases. The boiler has one top steam drum, 3ft. in diameter and 28ft. long, the fire-box being formed of banks of tubes passing downwards to two lower water drums, 18in. diameter and 11ft. long. The front part is formed of further tubes passing to two water drums, 19in. diameter by 13ft. 6in. long, placed at a higher level than the others. A superheater is fitted in the front end of the main flue.

The high pressure inside cylinders drive the front coupled axle, and are placed well forward, while the low-pressure outside pair drive the second axle. At starting, steam limited to 200 lbs. pressure can be admitted to the low-pressure cylinders. The tractive effort is estimated at 32,000 lbs.

The main particulars are : cylinders, two high-pressure, 10in. diameter by 26in. stroke ; two low-pressure, 20in. diameter by 26in. stroke ; coupled wheels, 6ft. 8in. diameter ; carrying wheels, front and rear, 3ft. 2in. diameter. Total heating surface, 2,126 sq. ft. As the top of the boiler is carried to the limit allowed by the loading gauge, no chimney can be permitted to project above it, and this is concealed except in a front view, by two metal wings formed by an extension of the smoke-box.

In 1920 an experimental geared steam turbine condensing loco-motive built by the Aktiebolaget Ljungstroms Angturbin, near Stock-holm, was tried out on the Swedish railways. This comprised two vehicles, one of which, with a two-axle bogie and three carrying axles, takes the boiler, and the other, with three motor axles and one truck axle, takes the main driving machinery and condensing plant.

The locomotive boiler has a heating surface of 108 sq. ft. in the fire-box and 1,130 sq. ft. in the tubes, with a grate area of 28 sq. ft. and a working pressure of 300 lbs. per sq. in. It is fitted with a superheater and with a hot air induced draught apparatus, the air heater for which is located beneath the front end of the boiler. The driver's cab and the coal bunkers are placed saddlewise across the boiler. The turbine is rated to develop 1,800 B.h.p. at 9,200 revolutions per minute, corresponding to a train speed of 68.3 miles an hour, the power transmitted through gearing having a ratio of 22 to 1 to the six-coupled driving wheels by means of connecting rods.

Exhaust steam from the turbine is led to a receiver and thence to the air-cooled surface condenser, consisting of flattened tubes in series, the cooling air for which is supplied by fans. The condensate is returned to the boiler by a boiler-feed pump through a series of feed-water heaters, which receive the requisite supply of exhaust steam from the auxiliaries at varying pressures, thus ensuring a high temperature of feed-water at the boiler. Under actual service conditions the results appear to have been highly satisfactory and showed a saving in fuel consumption of 50%.

In spite of its advantages, the complication and cost of the condensing arrangement prevented a more extended adoption of this form of turbine locomotive. The Ljungstrom Company therefore designed a non-condensing locomotive, having a 2,000 h.p. turbine arranged in front of the smoke-box and connected to the driving wheels by means of side rods through a gear and jack-shaft arrangement. The engine is of the 2-8-0 type, with coupled wheels 4ft. 5⅛in. diameter, with a four-wheeled tender, and is in service on the Grangesberg Railway, Sweden. Apart from the turbine and its accessories, the design of the locomotive is on similar lines to the orthodox reciprocating type engine. Steam from the boiler at 185 lbs. pressure passes through a regulator in the dome, thence through a superheater steam chest and strainer, to the admission valve bolted to the casing of the turbine. This admission valve is provided with five nozzles operated from the footplate. The regulator, therefore, is only used as a main stop valve for the boiler, and is opened full at the start of the run, and closed at the end. The tractive force is 47,400 lbs.

CHAPTER V

LOCOMOTIVES FOR MOUNTAINOUS COUNTRIES

POWERFUL locomotives are necessary in mountainous countries where steep and long gradients are traversed. Besides special classes of huge tank and tender engines, most of which have one or more pairs of wheels without flanges to ease running on sharp curves, in many instances a flexible or articulated type of locomotive is required to meet the special conditions of working.

Ordinary adhesion steam engines are employed on the 1 in 25 grade extending for 74 miles on the Callao-Oroya section of the standard gauge Central Railway of Peru, on the 1 in 28 narrow gauge Darjeeling Himalayan Railway, and on a 1 in 12 section of the Leopoldina Railway of Brazil. There are quite a variety of articulated locomotives for adhesion working, in which two or more units —each steam driven—are connected together in such a way that one can take up an angular position with respect to another section without difficulty when rounding sharp curves, especially on lines which have heavy traffic which must be hauled by large, long and powerful engines. In these circumstances the articulated locomotive alone meets the case.

SWING-BRIDGE OVER THE GLOUCESTER & BERKELEY CANAL AT SHARPNESS, SEVERN & WYE JOINT RAILWAY. (*Photo : Topical Agency.*)

For the purpose of connecting the Severn & Wye Railway, in the Forest of Dean district of Gloucestershire, with the former Midland Railway at Sharpness, a remarkable bridge was built across the river Severn, and opened in October, 1879. At the time of building it was, with the exception of the Tay Bridge, the longest bridge in the country, there being twenty-two spans. Two spans over the navigable channel are 327ft. long, and there are also five spans of 171ft., fourteen of 124ft., and one of 200ft., the latter being shown in our illustration. This is a swinging span over the Gloucester & Berkeley Canal worked by a steam engine, housed on top of the girders. The total length of the bridge is 1,387 yards, the width of the river being 1,186 yards. The bridge carries a single line of railway, but the swinging span has been built to accommodate two tracks, if necessary.

WHITEMOOR MARSHALLING YARD, NEAR MARCH, LONDON & NORTH EASTERN RAILWAY. (*Photo : L.N.E.R.*)

About thirty miles north of Cambridge, at Whitemoor, the London & North Eastern Railway have provided a concentration yard for dealing with freight traffic from the coal producing and manufacturing districts to East Anglia and London. The sidings illustrated deal with the south-bound traffic. It consists of two main sections ; ten reception roads, into which the trains to be sorted are run on arrival, and forty classification sidings, into which each train is sorted out, and these two parts are connected by the " hump."

On the arrival of a train, the shunter passes down the train, and makes a list, noting the destination of each wagon, and marking the " cut " according to the siding in which each wagon is to be dropped ; at the same time, he uncouples the wagons between the various cuts. He despatches a copy to the control cabin, and a copy is also given to the foreman at the top of the hump. When all is ready the shunting engine commences to push the train up over the hump at such a speed that a train of sixty or seventy wagons, having, say, forty cuts, can be disposed of in six or seven minutes. The hump is designed to provide momentum to carry wagons into the sorting sidings. Four hydraulic rail brakes are provided at the foot of the hump, one on each of the first four leads after the main points. They slow down the wagons, which are travelling too fast, and keep a suitable spacing between them.

SHIPPING A " SENTINEL " STEAM LOCOMOTIVE FOR SOUTH AMERICA. (*Photo : Sentinel Waggon Works.*)

Of late years the usual practice in delivering locomotives for overseas railways is to send them in shiploads, fully erected, ready to be put into service immediately on arrival at destination.

The accompanying illustration shows a six-engined Sentinel steam locomotive being loaded for shipment to a metre-gauge railway in Colombia, South America. It will be noticed this is being lifted by a derrick on the vessel itself, capable of taking lifts up to 120 tons.

STREAM-LINED 4-6-4 TYPE LOCOMOTIVE, NEW YORK CENTRAL LINES, U.S.A.

The first American stream-lined steam locomotive has been named *Commodore Vanderbilt,* after the founder of the New York Central Lines, and is of the Central's famous 4-6-4 Hudson type of passenger locomotives. Both locomotive and tender have been stream-lined in accordance with the latest researches in aero-dynamic science. In addition to the wheels of the tender and engine trucks, the 6ft. 7in. driving wheels are provided with roller bearings.

240 H.P. COVENTRY RAILCAR ON THE LONDON, MIDLAND & SCOTTISH RAILWAY.

One of the latest types of pneumatic tyred rail-car has recently been brought over from France, and tried on the main line of the London, Midland & Scottish Railway. It is a 56-seater, with a 240 h.p. petrol engine and mechanical transmission driving on one of the two eight-wheeled bogies. The wheels are fitted with pneumatic tyres, having steel flanges, and any loss of pressure in a tyre causes a hooter to sound in the driving cab. On a test run from Leighton Buzzard to Euston, $40\frac{1}{4}$ miles, were covered in $42\frac{1}{2}$ minutes, with a maximum speed at Watford of 66 miles per hour. The running of the car is particularly steady and silent.

ROYAL TRAIN, SOUTH AUSTRALIAN GOVERNMENT RAILWAYS.

When making his recent tour of the Australian Commonwealth, H.R.H. the Duke of Gloucester travelled over the 5ft. 3in. gauge lines of the South Australian Railways in a train replete with every possible convenience. The lounge of the Royal Saloon is equipped with radio, fans, clock and electric speedometer. It weighs 52 tons, and is approximately 80ft. long. Adjoining the lounge are three sleeping compartments, one having a beautifully appointed bathroom. The kitchen is also nicely fitted up and provided with hot and cold water, a wood burning stove, and an electric refrigerator of ample capacity. Finally, the dining-room, which is of plain design, is well finished, and lighted electrically by fittings flush with the roof of the car.

6-CYLINDER GARRATT LOCOMOTIVE, No. 2395, LONDON & NORTH EASTERN RAILWAY.

For " banking " heavy mineral trains on the Worsboro' branch, in South Yorkshire, which has a gradient of 1 in 40 for two miles, the London & North Eastern Railway use the most powerful locomotive in the British Isles. This is of the six-cylinder Garratt articulated type, built in 1925 by Beyer, Peacock & Co., Ltd., of Manchester. The engine is of the 2-8-0 + 0-8-2 type, each unit being a 2-8-0 three-cylinder engine, with the same cylinders, valve motion, etc., as those of the London & North Eastern Railway standard mineral engines.

D

The " Fairlie " double engine, of which about half a dozen were built for standard gauge railways in this country, in addition to a few for the Festiniog Railway (1ft. 11½in. gauge), provided a type with large tractive force, capable of passing round sharp curves. The whole of the weight was available for adhesion. The engine had a double boiler, each part with an independent fire-box, both boxes being in one casing and fired from the side. The boilers were carried on two steam bogies by means of saddles under which the pivots formed part of the bogie frames. The steam pipes were led into a special fitting forming a prolongation of the lower part of the smoke-box. Here a swivelling and sliding joint was provided through which steam passed to the cylinders by the centres of the bogies where these pipes were articulated. Ball and socket joints were also provided on the exhaust pipes. Many " Fairlie " locomotives were supplied to Mexico, Burma, New Zealand, Chili, Portugal, Russia, etc.

The " Mallet " locomotive, the most highly-developed articulated locomotive in the world for heavy freight service, was patented in the early 'eighties by Anatole Mallet, a famous French engineer. In the " Mallet " engine, which is really a semi-articulated one, the boiler and cab are fixed rigidly to the rear motor bogie, the front motor bogie being close coupled to the rear motor bogie by a vertical hinge pin, the centre of which is fixed at a point midway between the two sets of wheels, thus assisting the guiding of the rear bogie into curves. The boiler attached to the rear bogie protrudes forward over the front engine, the weight being taken by bearings on the front engine. A spring centring device on the boiler bearing assists recovery on leaving curves. The cylinders are located at the front of the motor bogies, the high pressure being fixed to the rear unit, and thus integral with the boiler and the low-pressure cylinders at the front of the engine. Large " Mallet " locomotives have been built by Continental and British builders, but its great development has been brought about in the United States. Long distances between important centres and heavy traffics have fostered its adoption there. Some large size " Mallets " of recent years are fitted with four high-pressure cylinders.

On the Virginian Railroad are some huge 2-10+10-2 " Mallet " engines, built for working coal trains of nearly 5,000 tons on the heavy grades over the Blue Ridge Mountains. Since the electrification of this line these engines act as bankers at the back of 14,000 ton coal trains, which are headed by one of the most powerful electric locomotives in the world.

The Erie Railroad have a Triplex " Mallet "—that is, with three sets of coupled wheels—and on a test run it hauled a load of about 15,000 tons, but a banking pilot was necessary to start the train.

Another articulated type is the " Kitson-Meyer," the first of which were built in this country in 1894. This has a single boiler carried by a girder supported by the steam bogies   There are two sets of coupled wheels below it, each with its own cylinders arranged at the outer ends of the bogies. In the early " Meyer " locomotives the cylinders were located at the centre of the engine. Among recent examples built for the Kalka-Simla Railway (India) and the Colombian National Railways, the bogies are arranged well apart, and special provision is made for ensuring maximum flexibility, not only in the horizontal but in the vertical direction.

As a special purpose articulated locomotive and a very efficient one, mention should be made of the " Shay " locomotive, first built in 1880. It is suitable for severe grades and sharp curves which cannot be economically worked by the ordinary adhesion type locomotive. Designed for duty in North American lumber camps it soon passed to other useful spheres, and has been extensively used for contractors' work and industrial establishments. In this locomotive the vertical engines are placed on one side of the centre line for balancing purposes and are strongly supported on the frame. Three cylinders are generally used, so as to bring the setting of the cranks to 120°. These drive on a crank shaft, which in turn is connected with the main longitudinal shaft, which is built in sections and rendered flexible by universal joints. The shaft drives pinions which mesh with bevel wheels attached to the outer face of the running wheels, so that every wheel is a driver. The engines are situate alongside the boiler, the latter being placed " off centre " sufficiently to balance the locomotive.

Combined rack and adhesion locomotives with two sets of engines are in successful service on some lines. One pair of cylinders drives the smooth wheels, and the second pair the rack mechanism, both sets being worked simultaneously on rack sections requiring maximum tractive power. On the Furka-Oberalp Railway (metre gauge), one of the few lines still worked by steam locomotives in Switzerland, combined rack and adhesion compound engines of the 2-6-0 type are used. In addition to the three-coupled axles for work on the adhesion sections of the line, driven by outside high-pressure cylinders, there are two inside coupled axles supported by internal longitudinal framing for driving the rack pinions ; these are driven by the low-pressure cylinders placed inside. The locomotive works as a " simple " engine on the adhesion sections of the line, and as a compound on the rack sections. To provide sufficient space for the large low-pressure cylinders the main framing is placed outside the wheels.

Purely rack locomotives are used where the ruling grade is practically continuous for the whole length of the railway. On the rack railways of Switzerland and other mountainous countries the old system introduced by Blenkinsop as far back as 1812 is revived. The object is the same, namely, to increase the tractive power with the minimum dead-weight of the engine. The rack is placed centrally between the ordinary rails, and in the Abt system two rack bars (and sometimes three) are used, and the method of laying these, one in advance of the other, differentiates the position of the teeth, and ensures smooth running.

For the first rack mountain railway—that from Vitznau, on Lake Lucerne—up the Rigi to Kulm, 5,905ft. above sea-level, a decided variation from orthodox design was made in the special type of locomotive, which like the railway itself was an entirely new departure. It was provided with a vertical boiler set at such an angle as to reduce, as far as possible, variations in the water level, due to the difference in gradients. After a few years service, this vertical boiler was abandoned in favour of the horizontal pattern, but this also has the appearance of tilting forward, because changes in the water level have to be allowed for. The grade of the Rigi is 1 in 4 for a large proportion of the way.

CHAPTER VI

FAMOUS TRAINS

DURING the past few years there has been a general speeding up of the main line railway services of this country, as well as those of the more important railways of Western Europe and several Overseas and Colonial lines, especially those of the United States and Canada. The narrow gauge systems of South Africa, New Zealand, Java and Japan have also accelerated their important trains.

It is for advertising purposes that certain expresses running long distances are given names that appeal to the general public. The oldest is the *Flying Scotsman* of the L. & N.E.R., which commenced running in June, 1862. The down train has left King's Cross ever since, at 10 o'clock every week-day morning for Grantham, York, Newcastle, Berwick and Edinburgh ; the up train leaves Waverley Station, Edinburgh, at the same time for King's Cross, making an additional stop at Darlington. Since 1928, during the summer months, the train runs non-stop in both directions—the world's record daily non-stop run of $392\frac{3}{4}$ miles.

D 2

The trains are made up of nine 6oft. cars, and a restaurant car set of three articulated coaches. The order, beginning from the engine, at King's Cross, being a third-class brake and a first and third composite for Perth, a third-class car, third-class restaurant-car, kitchen-car, first-class restaurant-car with cocktail bar, composite and third-class car, with hairdressing saloon, for Edinburgh, and composite, third-class and large brake for Aberdeen. Roughly, when loaded, the weight is 550 tons behind the engine tender.

Other important Anglo-Scottish expresses of the L. & N.E.R. include the "Highlandman," 7.25 p.m. ex King's Cross to Inverness and Fort William ; the "Aberdonian," 7.40 p.m., and the "Night Scotsman," 10.25 p.m. trains to Aberdeen.

The "Scarborough Flier" runs non-stop to York during the summer season. Leaving King's Cross at 11.10 a.m. it covers the 230 miles to Scarborough in four hours at 57.5 miles an hour.

By way of Leeds and Harrogate the "Queen of Scots" Pullman express leaves King's Cross at 11.20 a.m. and reaches Glasgow— $453\frac{1}{2}$ miles—in nine hours, and the "West Riding" Pullman, by the same route, departs from King's Cross at 4.45 p.m., of which one portion arrives at Newcastle—280.8 miles—in 5 hrs. 38 mins., and the other at Halifax—202.8 miles—in 4 hrs. 12 mins.

From Liverpool Street the 10 a.m. "Flushing Continental," 7.42 p.m., "Esbjerg Continental," 8.15 p.m., "Hook of Holland Continental," and 8.30 p.m. "Antwerp Continental," all connect with the cross-Channel boat services, and cover the 69 miles between London and Parkeston Quay, Harwich, at an average speed of over 50 miles an hour, over a very heavy road. On Sundays the "Clacton Pullman" from Liverpool Street, at 9.55 a.m., is a popular fast train to the East Coast resort, the $70\frac{3}{4}$ miles being covered in 97 minutes. During the summer this train forms the "Eastern Belle," which is run on week-days to seaside resorts on the East Coast.

On May 7th, 1903, the G.W.R. ran a 250 ton train hauled by

the 4-4-0 engine, *City of Bath*, from Plymouth to Paddington, 246¾ miles in 233½ minutes—i.e. 63.3 m.p.h. Just twelve months later the 4-4-0 locomotive, *City of Truro* (now preserved at the York Railway Museum), brought the American Mail over the same route as far as Bristol, and made a wonderful run. Exeter was passed dead slow in just under 56 minutes from North Road, Plymouth, a distance of 52 miles three chains over one of the heaviest roads in the country. Then followed a climb to Whiteball summit at a speed never below 62 m.p.h. Coming down the Wellington Bank a maximum speed of 102.3 m.p.h. was attained, the highest speed ever reached in this country by a steam train until the L. & N.E.R. made its record run at 108 m.p.h. on March 5th last, with the " Pacific " type locomotive, *Papyrus*. From Bristol to London the train was hauled by the 4-2-2 engine, *Duke of Connaught*, with 7ft. 8in. driving wheels, which maintained an average speed of 78 m.p.h. between Wootton Bassett and Westbourne Park—81¾ miles.

These runs were the prelude to the introduction in March, 1932, of the famous " Cheltenham Flyer," until lately the fastest steam-worked train in the world, which with unfailing regularity makes the journey from Swindon to Paddington, six days out of seven, in 65 minutes, a start to stop speed of 71.4 m.p.h. Frequently the train reaches Paddington in front of time. On one of its runs the speed of 87½ miles an hour was maintained for 70 miles of the journey, 28 of which were covered at a speed of 92.3 m.p.h.

In three months the " Flyer " only lost 7½ minutes on its schedule timing. During the first ten months of its running the total time lost was 634 minutes for 306 journeys, an average of 2-1/10th minutes per journey. It was on time 172 trips, and 134 times late owing to heavy traffic and fog. The load is generally six to eight corridor coaches, with dining car facilities, making a weight of 190 to 250 tons, and seating 250 to 364 without the dining car (35 seats).

THE "CORNISH RIVIERA LIMITED," G.W.R.—Until the
L. & N.E.R., in 1928, started the non-stop run of the "Flying Scotsman," the record for the longest run without halt was held for nearly
a quarter of a century by the "Cornish Riviera Limited," of the
G.W.R., the famous "10.30 Limited," the distance between Paddington and North Road Station, Plymouth, being 225¾ miles. Of course
there was a break in the run during the war period.

Since the completion of the Westbury and Frome by-pass lines,
during the summer service, on Mondays to Fridays the train runs
non-stop between London and Truro, 279 miles, and on Saturdays
the non-stop run is extended to St. Erth, a distance of 299 miles. A
stop is made at Exeter during the winter months, when slip portions
for Westbury and Taunton are carried. The timing London to
Plymouth (including the stop) is then only 4 hrs. 4 mins.

During the summer this train is followed from Paddington at
10.35 a.m. by "The Cornishman," which caters for the intermediate
traffic not served by the "Cornish Riviera Limited."

"ROYAL SCOT" EXPRESS, L.M. & S.R.—For over 70 years an
express train for Scotland, now known as the "Royal Scot," has left
Euston Station at 10 a.m., the West Coast replica of the East Coast's
"Flying Scotsman." The time taken by both routes is approximately
identical. The "Royal Scot" hold the world's record for the longest
non-stop run all the year round—Carlisle to London—299 miles. The
long journey, with its climb over Shap (915ft.), affords an exacting
test of locomotive performance.

As the L.M. & S. main line does not run both to Glasgow and
Edinburgh, the train is made up of two sections which on the down
journey diverge at Carstairs, although they are actually divided at
Symington, 6¾ miles south of the junction. Engines are changed at
Kingmoor, just over 300 miles from Euston. On April 27th, 1928,
when the traffic was exceptionally heavy, the two sections were run
separately throughout and for the first time the Glasgow portion ran

non-stop Euston to Glasgow, 401½ miles, the longest non-stop run that has ever been attempted.

From St. Pancras the " Thames & Forth Express " at 9 a.m. via Nottingham, Leeds and Carlisle and then over the Waverley route via Galashiels to Edinburgh, covers the 408.8 miles in 8 hrs. 52 mins., and the " Thames & Clyde Express " from St. Pancras at 10 a.m. via Leicester, Leeds and Kilmarnock to St. Enoch, Glasgow, makes the 426 miles journey in 8 hrs. 50 mins.

In Scotland the L.M. & S., among other important trains, run the " Granite City," between Glasgow and Aberdeen, and from Inverness the " John o' Groats " to Wick, and the " Hebridean " and " Lewisman " to the Kyle of Lochalsh, in connection with the boats.

THE " IRISH MAIL "—The train which left Euston Station at 8.45 p.m. on August 1st, 1848, was called the " Irish Mail," and has been so named ever since. At that date the Britannia Tubular Bridge across the Menai Straits was not built, so that the mails and passengers had to take coach from Bangor to Llanfair, in Anglesey, by way of the Suspension Bridge, where another train awaited them. When the train arrived at Holyhead, at 7.5 a.m., the Admiralty took charge of the mails and delivered them at Kingstown Pier at about 11.30 a.m. By June, 1850, on completion of the Britannia Bridge, the train was accelerated by one hour, and the mail reached Kingstown by 10.30 a.m. The apparatus for picking up and dropping mail bags from a moving train had, by 1854, reached a state of sufficient dependability to permit of it being worked at a speed of over 40 miles an hour, thus obviating the necessity of stopping the mail trains at a large number of relatively unimportant stations.

There has been a second mail train almost from the beginning of railway communication. The down train did not leave London in the morning as now, but at 5 p.m., and the steamer in connection reached Kingstown at about 6 o'clock in the morning. Later acceleration brought the 8.45 p.m. mail into Dublin in time to catch the

" Irish Mail " trains, and the afternoon mail became the morning mail of to-day.

By the contract of 1860 between the Post Office, the L. & N.W.R. and the City of Dublin Steam Packet Company, the trains had to cover the 264 miles between London and Holyhead (Admiralty Pier) at an average speed of 42 miles an hour, and it was to enable the " Irish Mail " to pick up water without stopping that troughs were laid between the rails near Aber for the first time in the world, in 1861. Hence, in 1863, the " Irish Mail " was the fastest train out of Euston, and noted for its remarkable good time keeping. A reduction of about 20 minutes in the running time took place ten years later, and in 1875 sleeping cars were introduced.

In 1880 the inner harbour at Holyhead was completed. At this time the sorting of the mail was largely carried out on the steamer ; nowadays all the sorting is performed on the train.

In 1920 the mail contract passed to the L. & N.W.R., and thence, in 1923, to the L.M. & S.R.

The steamers on the service, the *Cambria*, *Hibernia*, and *Scotia* twin-screw, with turbine engines, have a tonnage of 3,400 and a speed of 25 knots. There are only two faster merchant vessels than these.

In 1850 the average time to carry the mails between London and Dublin was $14\frac{1}{2}$ hours. To-day the Down Day service is $9\frac{1}{4}$ hours, and the Down Night, 9 hrs. 50 mins. ; the Up Day, 9 hrs. 10 mins., and the Up Night, 9 hrs. 20 mins. On the summer day schedule, Saturdays only, the train leaves Holyhead Harbour at 12.27 p.m., and runs non-stop to Euston, which is reached at 5.30 p.m.—$263\frac{3}{4}$ miles in 303 minutes.

The Postal Trains, or Mails, were the fastest and most important in the country in years gone by. Passengers were conveyed by them, but often only first class, or first and second class, and a supplementary charge made. To-day the postal business has grown so that on the main routes trains, made up entirely of sorting and storage vans, are run by night, and every attention is concentrated on the maintenance of absolute punctuality. The most important of the British postal trains is undoubtedly the West Coast Postal, which for many years has left Euston for Scotland by the L.M. & S. route at 8.30 p.m.

The more important London to Manchester and Liverpool expresses are named. The " Comet " follows the main line to Crewe, where it branches off to Manchester ; the " Merseyside " and " Manxman " both run to Crewe and Liverpool. The " Mancunian " runs from Euston to Manchester via Crewe, and returns via Stoke-on-Trent, whereas the " Lancastrian " does the reverse.

Mention should also be made of the " Sunny South " express from Liverpool and Manchester to the South Coast resorts, through Addison Road and Clapham Junction, also the " Pines " express from Liverpool to Bournemouth via Bath.

Then there is the " Ulster Express " from Euston to Heysham, for the Belfast boats, and the " Lakes Express " to Windermere. Along the Holyhead line, besides the two Irish Mails, there is the " Welshman," and a number of summer expresses to North Wales.

THE " ATLANTIC COAST EXPRESS," SOUTHERN RAILWAY.—One of the finest trains of this country is the " Atlantic Coast Express," which leaves Waterloo Station on week-days at 11 o'clock a.m. for North Cornwall and North Devon. It is made up of the latest type steel-panelled corridor cars, with numbered seats for reservation purposes, and large restaurant cars. This train is invariably worked by one of the " Lord Nelson " or " King Arthur " class locomotives, and in the summer on its run from London to Exeter makes but one stop—Salisbury—covering the first stage of $83\frac{3}{4}$ miles in 90 minutes. The second stage from Salisbury to Exeter is 88 miles, including the formidable bank of 1 in 80 for $4\frac{1}{2}$ miles, to the Honiton tunnel, which is $\frac{3}{4}$ of a mile long, still rising at 1 in 132. The time taken for the $171\frac{3}{4}$ miles (including 6 minutes stop at Salisbury) from London to Exeter is 3 hrs. 13 mins.

The "Continental Pullman Boat Express" of the S.R. leaves Victoria at 11 a.m. daily, and reaches the Marine Station at Dover, $77\frac{1}{2}$ miles, in 93 minutes.   The corridor coaches used for this service are 64ft. long over gangways, constructed to work in connection with the Pullman cars, and are fitted with vestibules and automatic couplers.

The "Brighton Belle," over the electrified line between Victoria and Brighton, covers the 51 miles in 60 minutes and makes three double journeys daily, and is one of the most popular all-Pullman services, catering for first and third class passengers.   It is usually made up of a five-car set, seating 40 first and 152 third class passengers.

The "Bournemouth Belle" Pullman express runs on Sundays only in the winter, with extra trips at holiday times, and daily in the summer.   Leaving Waterloo at 10.30 a.m., it reaches Bournemouth West, $111\frac{1}{2}$ miles, in 2 hrs. 22 mins.

Other S.R. Pullman trains from Victoria are the "Eastbourne Sunday Limited," to Lewes and Eastbourne, and "The Thanet Pullman Limited," to Margate, Broadstairs and Ramsgate.

CHAPTER VII

LONDON, MIDLAND AND SCOTTISH RAILWAY

WITH a route mileage of 7,790 and a track mileage, including sidings, of 20,100 and more than 2,500 stations, the L.M. & S. lines reach to Southend, Lincoln and Goole on the east side of England, to Bournemouth in the south, Swansea in South Wales, and to Edinburgh, Aberdeen, Inverness and Wick in Scotland, besides a detached system in the North of Ireland.   It is the largest of the four railway groups, and comprises the former London & North Western, Midland, Lancashire & Yorkshire, North Staffordshire, Maryport & Carlisle, Furness, Caledonian, Glasgow & South Western, and Highland systems, as well as numerous subsidiary lines.

It is the biggest organization in the British Empire, excepting only the Post Office, for it gives employment to 230,000 people, has a capital of £425,000,000 and has about £30,000,000 invested in locomotive plant.

In 1935 the L.M. & S.R. owned nearly 8,000 locomotives, hauling about 20,000 passenger coaches, and nearly 300,000 freight vehicles. It also possessed 80 steamships of various kinds.

At the time of its formation, in 1846, the L. & N.W.R. had a mileage of rather over 400 miles, and comprised the London & Birmingham, Grand Junction and Manchester & Birmingham Railways. The famous Liverpool & Manchester and London & Birmingham Railways may, however, be looked upon as the forbears of the L. & N.W.R., which, in turn, became such an important constituent of the L.M. & S.R.

The L. & M.R. was opened for traffic on September 15th, 1830, the year after the Rainhill trials, in which Stephenson's *Rocket* gained the prize of £500. Although part of the Bolton & Leigh Railway was opened on August 1st, 1828, and later became part of the Grand Junction, there is little doubt that the L. & M. was the real origin of the L. & N.W.R. The L. & M. was the first railway to be opened with the definite intention of using locomotives throughout. Two days after the opening a service of passenger trains was started, although a similar service was not provided on the Stockton & Darlington Railway until 1833, passengers on that line, with the exception of the opening day, September 27th, 1825, having been conveyed by horse traction. The construction of the line was a difficult task, among the undertakings being the crossing of the treacherous bogs of Chat Moss and Parr Moss, the building of the Sankey viaduct of nine arches of 50ft. span, the Olive Mount cutting of two miles length and 80ft. deep, and finally a tunnel under Liverpool to the station at Crown Street. It was not until some years later that the extension to Lime Street, Liverpool, was undertaken.

Apart from branches connecting with the L. & M. made by independent companies and afterwards absorbed by the L. & N.W., the next important schemes were the Grand Junction and the London & Birmingham, both sanctioned in 1833.

The original object of the Grand Junction Railway was to connect Liverpool, Manchester and Preston with Birmingham, but by joining up with the L. & B.R., these northern towns were brought within reach of the Metropolis. By means of the Warrington & Newton Railway (opened in 1833) the Grand Junction had a main line, from Warrington to Birmingham (78 miles) and opened July 4th, 1837. In September of the following year the L. & B. was opened throughout. Trains from the south were then divided at Warrington, half going to Liverpool and half to Manchester. Engineering works on the Grand Junction included viaducts over the Mersey at Warrington, and over the Irwell Canal, and the Dutton and Royal Vale viaducts over the Weaver. At Birmingham the line was carried on a ten-arched viaduct and terminated in Curzon Street.

The L. & B. was the first trunk line out of London, with a length of $112\frac{1}{2}$ miles. George Stephenson and his son, Robert, were the engineers, and it is to their energy and skill that the difficulties in construction were overcome. Of the eight tunnels which had to be made, the Kilsby—2,426 yards in length—is reckoned the greatest work on the line, costing £125 per yard, or more than three times what had been estimated. Disastrous flooding, due to a strata of greensand which trial shafts had failed to locate, delayed the boring for eight months, pending the removal of the water by pumps working at the rate of 2,000 gallons a minute. The determination to build as level a line as possible involved the excavation of a deep cutting at Tring, $2\frac{1}{2}$ miles long, and at Roade, $1\frac{1}{2}$ miles long, and erection of viaducts at Watford, Weedon, Wolverton and Birmingham. Two other tunnels of note were those at Primrose Hill and at Watford, 1,182 yards, and 1,800 yards respectively.

It was intended to have the London terminus at Camden, but this was abandoned in favour of extending it to Euston, involving the steep inclines of 1 in 70 and 1 in 77 when leaving that station. This portion was originally worked by rope haulage, the stationary engines for which were on either side of the line at the top of the bank.

Euston terminus, with its imposing Doric arch, was completed in 1839. The Birmingham terminus was at Curzon Street, now a goods station, with the Grand Junction terminus near by. The present New Street Station, Birmingham, was opened in 1852.

The other large partner in the L. & N.W. fusion was the Manchester & Birmingham Railway, which connected Manchester with Crewe, and opened on August 10th, 1842. A fine viaduct of twenty arches carried the line out of Manchester, and approaching Stockport was another viaduct of 22 arches. The Bollin viaduct of 11 arches, and Dane of 23 arches deserve mention. A branch to Macclesfield opened in 1845 included the Prestbury and Macclesfield tunnels (260 and 342 yards respectively).

After the formation of the L. & N.W.R., the first development was the opening of the Trent Valley line from Rugby to Stafford, in 1847, now part of the West Coast route to Scotland. This link reduced the distance between London and the North by avoiding Birmingham, and its importance may be estimated by the fact that it is now four-tracked almost throughout. At this date the L. & N.W. ended at Preston, the trains northwards going by the Lancaster & Preston (opened 1840), the Lancaster & Carlisle (opened 1846), and the Caledonian. The two first mentioned lines were absorbed by the L. & N.W. in 1859 and 1879 respectively. Among the engineering features on the Lancaster and Carlisle section mention should be made of the cutting at Shap summit—6oft. deep ; the Lowther viaduct, near Penrith, with six arches of 6oft. span ; and another viaduct, near the same place, of five 5oft. arches, over the River Eamont. There are steep gradients, both in the down and in

THREE-CYLINDER 4-4-0 " SCHOOLS " CLASS PASSENGER LOCOMOTIVE, SOUTHERN RAILWAY. (Photo: W. J. Reynolds.)

Engine No. 908, *Westminster*, is one of a numerous class which the Southern Railway have built at their Eastleigh Works for use on main lines to the seaside resorts of Kent, served by the Eastern section, as well as for the Isle of Wight services to Portsmouth on the Western section.   The heavy gradients on the Hastings line and the increasing weight of modern rolling stock necessitate providing a really powerful locomotive, which at the same time must be kept as small and compact as possible to clear the restricted loading gauges of the tunnels.   This problem has been solved by this locomotive, which weighs, with its tender, 110 tons.

Named after famous public schools, they are known as the " Schools " class. The round-top firebox has been adopted due to the limitations of weight, but it permits a good outlook for the driver.   Side windows are provided for the cab, while the look-out glasses on the driver's side are fitted with window wipers.

The three cylinders are $16\frac{1}{2}$in. diameter by 26in. stroke, and the driving wheels are 6ft. 7in. diameter.   The piston valves are driven by three sets of Walschaert valve gear.

The engine weighs 67.1 tons in working order, of which 42 tons rest on the coupled wheels.   The tender carries 4,000 gallons of water and 5 tons of coal.

SUPER-PACIFIC TYPE LOCOMOTIVE, No. 2750, " PAPYRUS," LONDON & NORTH EASTERN RAILWAY.   The Locomotive that holds the World's Speed Records. (Photo: W. J. Reynolds.)

Introduced in 1922, the three-cylinder Pacifics are the standard heavy express locomotives of the London & North Eastern Railway.

The striking feature of these engines is the huge boiler, which has a parallel front portion 5ft. 9in. outside diameter, followed by a tapered portion increasing to 6ft. 5in. diameter, the length between tube-plates being 19ft.   A very wide firebox is provided, the inner box extending into the barrel of the boiler.

The weight of the engine in working order is 92 tons 9 cwts., of which 60 tons rest on the coupled wheels.

It was one of the later super-Pacifics, No. 2750, *Papyrus*, built at Doncaster in 1929, that was selected for the experimental run on Tuesday, March 5th, 1935, which beat the world's record for speed made by a steam train, by running from London to Newcastle-on-Tyne under 4 hours, the distance being 268 miles, with a train weighing 213 tons and seating 204 passengers.   Leaving King's Cross at 9.8 a.m., Newcastle was reached at $1.4\frac{1}{2}$ p.m., nearly 4 mins. ahead of schedule.   At 3.47 p.m. the return journey was begun, and for over 12 miles, from Corby down the long drop from Stoke box to Tallington, the average speed was over 100 m.p.h., while just south of Little Bytham, 105.5 m.p.h. was registered for 30 seconds, and for 10 seconds it reached 108 m.p.h.   The whole journey from Newcastle to King's Cross was completed in 3 hrs. 51 mins., at an average of 69.6 miles per hour.   The train covered 536.4 miles in 7 hrs. $47\frac{1}{2}$ mins.

THREE-CYLINDER 4–6–0 EXPRESS PASSENGER ENGINE, No. 5552, " SILVER JUBILEE," LONDON, MIDLAND & SCOTTISH RAILWAY.

Over one hundred of these new standard 4-6-0 three-cylinder locomotives, designed by Mr. W. A. Stanier, chief mechanical engineer, of the L. M. & S. Railway, have been constructed. These handsome and efficient machines of which the example illustrated, No. 5552, was the first to be built at Crewe Works, have proved highly successful on the express services of the L. M. & S. Railway.

With the King's permission, this engine has now been named *Silver Jubilee*, and the class to which it belongs is known as the Jubilee Class. All the bright parts of the engine have been chromium-plated, and the paintwork is black, giving it a pleasing and dignified finish. The controls in the spacious and comfortable driver's cab are chromium-plated, against a background of white enamel.

4–4–0 THREE-CYLINDER COMPOUND EXPRESS LOCOMOTIVE, No. 87, " KESTREL," GREAT NORTHERN RAILWAY (IRELAND).

Between the cities of Dublin and Belfast the accelerated express services of the Great Northern Railway are worked by a very efficient class of three-cylinder compound locomotives, carrying a working pressure of 250 lbs. per sq. in. The system of compounding is the same as that so successfully used on the L. M. & S. Railway for trains up to 300-350 tons behind the tender. The Irish trains are generally lighter than in Great Britain, and since all coal is imported, fuel economy is a necessity, and superheating has been extensively applied by the G.N.R.

The inside high-pressure cylinder is $17\frac{1}{4}$in. by 26in. ; and the two outside low-pressure 19in. by 26in. The coupled wheels are 6ft. 7in. diameter. Heating surface is 1,251 sq. ft., and super-heater surface 276.5 sq. ft. Grate area 25.22 sq. ft. Tractive effort 23,762 lbs. at 80% boiler pressure in low-pressure cylinders. Weight : engine, 65 tons ; tender, $38\frac{1}{2}$ tons.

CONVERTED 2–8–2 TANK LOCOMOTIVE FOR MINERAL TRAFFIC, No. 7200, GREAT WESTERN RAILWAY.

Originally these engines were of the 2-8-0 type, and designed primarily for dealing with the South Wales coal traffic from the pits to the port of shipment. Owing, however, to the falling off in the export coal trade, in recent years, they were not required for this service, and have been converted at Swindon Works to the 2-8-2 type, with larger coal and water capacity, to make them suitable for longer runs on main line freight services. The new trailing radial truck has increased side play to enable sharp curves to be negotiated.

The leading particulars are : Two cylinders, 19in. diameter by 30in. stroke ; coupled wheels, 4ft. $7\frac{1}{2}$in. diameter ; leading truck wheels, 3ft. 2in. diameter ; trailing radial wheels, 3ft. 8in. diameter ; working pressure, 200 lbs. per sq. inch. Total heating surface, 1670.15 sq. ft. Grate area, 20.56 sq. ft. ; tank capacity, 2,500 gallons ; coal bunker 6 tons ; tractive effort, 33,170 lbs. Weight, in working order, 90 tons 12 cwts.

E

the up direction, to Shap summit. Down trains have to face $1\frac{1}{2}$ miles at 1 in 147, followed directly by $4\frac{1}{2}$ miles at 1 in 75, to the summit. Up trains, soon after leaving Penrith, have a nine miles climb, mostly at 1 in 125, before reaching the top.

The Chester & Holyhead Railway, which Robert Stephenson had completed in 1850, was acquired by the L. & N.W.R. in 1858. The Conway River and the Menai Straits were crossed in each case by wrought-iron tubular bridges. The one over the Straits, the celebrated Britannia Bridge, was the greater work of the two ; it is carried on three towers, the centre one built on the Britannia rock being 230ft. in height. Each of the side towers was 212ft. high, and the tubes from the abutments to each of these towers were of 230ft. span, while the four tubes from the central tower to the side towers on either side had a span of 460ft.

In 1862 the old Cromford and High Peak Railway was leased. It is an extremely hilly line, and had been opened in 1832. At first it was worked by horses ; and on the inclines—at 1 in $8\frac{1}{2}$—by stationary engines. Part has now been abandoned, and a small portion forms part of the Buxton and Ashbourne line, while the rest is used for goods only. It was amalgamated with the L. & N.W. in 1887.

The comparatively small but busy line of the North London Railway was brought under the management of the L. & N.W. in 1908, and under the grouping of the railways in 1923 became part of the L.M. & S.

At Crewe are located the largest locomotive works in the British Isles. Here, in addition to overhaul and repair work, one hundred to two hundred new engines are produced annually in normal times.

The Midland line ranked second in importance to the North Western in the L.M. & S. group. From small beginnings it grew to be one of the main trunk lines out of London. Reaching from St. Pancras, north to Carlisle, its numerous extensions include a second main route to Birmingham and Bristol. It served Leicester, Derby, Nottingham, Leeds, Malvern, Burton-on-Trent, Buxton, Barnsley, and Bradford, and by means of jointly owned lines, Manchester, Chester, Liverpool and Southport.

Its headquarters were at Derby, and here also were the very extensive locomotive and carriage works, and still one of the principal depots of the L.M. & S.R.

Unlike most of the main lines, the Midland reached the metropolis by coming south. At first, in 1840, it got no farther than Rugby, from which its traffic was conveyed over the L. & N.W.R. to Euston. Later, a line was made from Leicester by way of Bedford to Hitchin on the Great Northern Railway, and from 1857 the Midland ran its trains to King's Cross until 1868. In that year its own main line from Bedford to St. Pancras was completed and opened.

The lines leaving the main line are important, and several form main routes in themselves. Such is the section leaving Trent for Derby, through the Peak district, to Manchester, with a branch at Millers Dale, to Buxton, and connections over the Cheshire lines at Stockport for Warrington and Liverpool, and by a loop in Manchester to the Lancashire & Yorkshire Railway, thus bringing the large Lancashire towns in connection and providing an alternative route to the north, joining the Carlisle line at Hellifield.

Another important section is that in a southerly direction from Derby through Burton-on-Trent, Birmingham, Worcester, Cheltenham and Gloucester to Bristol, with a branch at Mangotsfield for Bath, and to the Somerset and Dorset joint line.

An off-shoot from the Northern main line, near Long Preston, took the Midland to Morecambe and Heysham, whence steamers run to Belfast and the Isle of Man. Electric traction was installed on the line between Lancaster and Morecambe and Heysham in 1908.

In 1912 the Midland Co. purchased the London, Tilbury & Southend Railway, first opened in 1854. This line extends from Gas Factory Junction ($2\frac{3}{4}$ miles from Fenchurch Street terminus, into which it has running powers) to Tilbury, Southend and Shoeburyness.

There is a ferry service from Tilbury to Gravesend. By the opening of the Tottenham & Forest Gate Railway, in 1899, the L.T. & S.R. was connected with the Midland ; and in 1902 the opening of the Whitechapel & Bow Railway brought it into communication with the District Railway.

In 1903 the Belfast & Northern Counties Railway was amalgamated with the Midland ; and this section is known as the " Northern Counties Committee, L.M. & S.R." This line has a mileage of 265, and is constructed to the Irish gauge of 5ft. 3in., except some branches which have a gauge of 3ft. The Midland also became part owners in 1906 of another Irish line—the Donegal Railway, of 3ft. gauge.

One of the most complicated systems in Great Britain is that of the former Lancashire & Yorkshire Railway, serving the southern portions of Lancashire and Yorkshire, and linking up the East Coast with the West from Goole to Liverpool. The main route for the fast trains from Liverpool and Manchester to Bradford and Leeds is the line running via Wigan, and on through Rochdale, Todmorden and Sowerby Bridge to Halifax, thence over the Great Northern to Leeds, with a short section taking off at Low Moor for Bradford.

The oldest portion of the L. & Y., which itself dates from 1847, is the Manchester & Bolton, opened in May, 1838, and the most important, the Manchester & Leeds, opened throughout in 1841.

At the Horwich Locomotive Works of the L. & Y., near Bolton, established in 1892, the principle of standardization has been carried out to a high degree, and this is still one of the chief establishments of the L.M. & S. for the construction and repair of engines. The L. & Y. was formally amalgamated with the L. & N.W. in 1921.

The Wirral Railway, a local line in the Birkenhead, New Brighton and West Kirby district of North Cheshire, was another small line, 14 miles in length, taken over by the L.M. & S. Also a small independent railway, 11½ miles long, between Garstang and Catterall stations, on the main line, and Knott End.

A mid-Anglian railway absorbed by the L.M. & S. was the Stratford-upon-Avon and Midland Junction. This was formed in 1909 by the fusion of three small lines—the East & West Junction, Stratford, Towcester & Midland Junction and Northampton & Banbury Junction Railways.

Among the rest of the English railways incorporated in the L.M. & S. system, mention should be made of the Cockermouth, Keswick & Penrith, in the Lake District. It was built jointly by the Stockton & Darlington and L. & N.W.R., and opened in 1865.

The Furness Railway, the first portion of which was opened in 1846, ran from Carnforth to Whitehaven, and was the only railway with access to the harbour and docks of Barrow-in-Furness. It was well-known for its connection with the Lakes, and served the Furness district of Lancashire and west coast of Cumberland.

The Maryport & Carlisle Railway was a small line in the same district. Laid out by George Stephenson, it was opened in 1845.

There is only one more English company of importance in the L.M. & S. group to mention, namely, the North Staffordshire Railway. It served the " Potteries " district, and also owned a considerable mileage of canals. The main sections are from Crewe, through Stoke to Burton and Derby, and from Colwich to Macclesfield.

The principal steamship services run by the L.M. & S. are the five routes connecting Great Britain and Ireland, between Holyhead and Dun Laoghaire (formerly Kingstown) ; Holyhead and Dublin (North Wall) and to Greenore for cargo and livestock only ; also between Heysham and Belfast, and between Stranraer and Larne.

The three Scottish partners in the L.M.S. group were the Caledonian, Glasgow & South Western and Highland Railways.

The oldest part of the Caledonian system—the Glasgow & Garnkirk—was a small line, opened in September, 1831, and purchased by them in 1846.

The Caledonian Railway itself was incorporated in 1845 for the
E 2

construction of a line from Carlisle to Edinburgh, and of another from near Gartsherrie to join the Scottish Central Railway, at Greenhill, from whence the C.R. reached Perth. Their first passenger station in Glasgow was at St. Rollox, and in 1849 the extension to the present station at Buchanan Street was made.

The route northward from Carlisle is almost direct to Carstairs, a point about midway between Edinburgh and Glasgow, although it involves the Beattock bank, which comprises two miles of 1 in 88, two of 1 in 80, and six of 1 in 75. The line was opened to Glasgow in February, 1848, together with the line from Carstairs Junction to Edinburgh. In the same year the Scottish Central line to Perth was opened, and this became amalgamated with the Caledonian in 1865, by which time the S.C.R. had absorbed the Dundee, Perth & Aberdeen Junction and the Dundee and Newtyle Railways. Another railway taken over by the C.R. in 1866, was the Scottish North Eastern, which was formed by the fusion of the Aberdeen and Scottish Midland Junction lines. Of the above mentioned railways the old D. & N. is of special interest. Opened in 1831, it had three inclined planes which were operated by stationary winding engines, while the level stretches were worked by horses. Locomotives were employed on the line from 1833. Various diversions of the original route have long since eliminated the inclines.

When the 1923 amalgamation took place, the main line of the Caledonian extended from Carlisle to Aberdeen via Carstairs, Stirling and Perth. From this the main routes to Edinburgh and Glasgow take off at Carstairs and Law Junctions respectively. From Glasgow and Edinburgh, similar lines join the main route at Glenboig and Larbert. Other branches are from Lockerbie to Dumfries ; Symington to Peebles ; Dunblane to Oban via Callender and Loch Awe ; Crieff Junction to Crieff, and thence to Perth ; and Perth to Dundee and Newtyle, Forfar, etc.

Next in importance to the Caledonian was the Glasgow & South Western Railway, formed in 1850 out of the Glasgow, Paisley,

Kilmarnock and Ayr Railway (opened in 1840) and the line from
Kilmarnock to Carlisle via Dumfries. It joined the C.R. at Gretna
Junction. The oldest portion of the G. & S.W. system is what was
formerly the Kilmarnock & Troon Railway, opened for horse traction
as early as 1811, and the first railway in Scotland. The G. & S.W.
worked the Midland trains from Carlisle to Glasgow. The Ayr line
was extended from Girvan to Challoch Junction in 1877, where it
joined the Portpatrick Railway, and afforded connection with Stranraer Harbour for the short sea route to Larne.

On the Dumfries line, near Mauchline, is the famous Balloch-
myle Viaduct. It is 630ft. long, and consists of six approach arches,
each of 50ft. span, and one central arch, the largest stone arch in the
world, having a span of 181ft. ; the highest point of this span is 157ft.
4in. above the River Ayr. On the same line is the Templand viaduct,
near Old Cumnock. It has fourteen 50ft. span arches, and five of
30ft. ; it is 145ft. 9in. from river to rail level.

The Highland Railway, although not quite so important as the
other Scottish partners in the L.M. & S. group, is nevertheless a line
of considerable interest. The line across the Grampians reaches at
the Pass of Drumuachdar, an altitude of 1,484ft. above sea-level, the
highest point of any main line in Great Britain. The Highland is
noteworthy for the reason it goes farther north than any other railway
in this country, viz. to Thurso, 722 miles from London.

The H.R. was formed in 1865, when the Inverness and Aberdeen
Junction and Inverness and Perth Junction Railways were amalgamated ; the extremities of these were Inverness, Keith and Perth.
The oldest part was the piece between Inverness and Nairn, opened
in 1855. The line beyond Inverness was made by the Ross-shire
Railway to Bonar Bridge in 1864, and the Sutherland Railway,
thence to Golspie in 1868. The line across Scotland from Dingwall
to Strome Ferry, to afford communication with Skye and the Hebrides,
was opened in 1870, and extended to Kyle of Lochalsh in 1897, from

which there is a service of steamers to Stornoway. The Duke of Sutherland built the line northwards from Golspie to Helmsdale in 1871, and the extreme north was reached by the Sutherland & Caithness Railway to Wick and Thurso. A further development was the building of a direct line from Aviemore to Inverness in 1898.

Among developments of recent years on the L.M. & S. system are the electrification of the suburban lines from Euston and Broad Street, London, out to Watford, and the branches to Kew Bridge, Richmond and Earl's Court, together with a section of the Southend line from Barking to Upminster. Another suburban electrified line is in the Manchester area, where the Manchester, South Junction & Altrincham Railway, which is jointly owned by the L.M. & S. and L. & N.E.R., and operated by the L.M. & S., was changed over to electric working in May, 1931. The L. & Y. adopted electrical working on the section between Liverpool and Southport in 1904, and also converted the line from Manchester to Bury a few years later.

CHAPTER VIII

LONDON AND NORTH EASTERN RAILWAY

OF the four British railway systems, the London & North Eastern takes second place, with a total route mileage of 6,721, or reduced to single track, 17,413 miles. It embraces the following seven railways : North Eastern, Great Northern, Great Central, Great Eastern, North British, Great North of Scotland, Hull & Barnsley, as well as many small ones. It serves a territory 600 miles long from the Thames to the Moray Firth, in addition to extensive areas in the centre and west, both of England and Scotland. It has 6,860 locomotives, 21,000 passenger train vehicles, and 275,000 freight wagons, and owns about 2,500 stations and goods depots. It has 16,000 road vehicles. The fleet of steamers numbers 40.

Some idea of the resources of the L. & N.E.R. may be gathered from the fact that it possesses 3,800 acres of water area, and 210 coal shipping berths. At Alloa, Bo'ness, Burntisland, Charlestown, Connah's Quay, Grimsby, Harwich, Hull, the Hartlepools, Immingham, London, Lowestoft, Mallaig, Methil, Middlesbrough, Silloth, Newcastle (Tyne Dock), Sunderland and Tayport, the Company owns docks and harbours of varying importance and directly serves many other well-known ports, including London, Manchester, Liverpool and Glasgow. The L. & N.E.R. operates Continental steamship services to and from Harwich and Grimsby, and owns a fleet of steamers serving the Firth of Clyde watering places.

The railways forming the L. & N.E.R. group can claim several innovations in railway travel. The first restaurant car ran on the G.N.R. in 1879, while the same company was also responsible for the introduction of articulated carriage stock, when, in 1913, they mounted two cars on three bogies.

As is well known, on September 27th, 1825, the S. & D.R.— 26¾ miles long—was opened amid great rejoicings. This, the first public railway in the world, operated by steam locomotives, is now part of the L. & N.E.R. George Stephenson, after a first survey for it, conducted a second in 1821. In the following year he was appointed engineer, and in that year the first rails were laid at Stockton by Mr. Thomas Meynell, the Chairman, 4ft. 8in. apart (subsequently widened to 4ft. 8½in. to allow for easier railway running).

Encouraged by the success of the S. & D. other railways were made in the North of England to take part in improving the means of transport. Most of the projects were from the coalfields to the sea, and it was some time before the main route north and south was completed. The Newcastle & Carlisle Railway—63 miles in length, and completed in 1839—was the first line connecting the east coast with the west coast.

The present main line northwards from York was built, in 1840, by the Great North of England Railway, and as far as Darlington is remarkable for its straightness and easy gradients, and well adapted for high speeds.   The Newcastle to Berwick line, opened in 1847, had some heavy engineering works.   The High Level Bridge, near the Tyne, at Newcastle-on-Tyne, 1,337ft. in length, and the Border Bridge, with its 28 stone arches, over the Tweed, at Berwick, 2,160ft., are both memorials of the genius of Robert Stephenson.   On the Church Fenton and Harrogate branch, opened 1848, is the viaduct of 31 arches, each 50ft. in span across the Crimple valley.

The N.E.R. was formed by the fusion, in 1854, of the York, Newcastle & Berwick, York & North Midland and Leeds Northern Railways, with headquarters at York.

The main line was straightened and shortened in 1868, by the making of the Team Valley line between Newcastle and Durham, and in 1871 by the direct Selby line, between Doncaster and York. This completed the main line, as we know it to-day, except that until 1877 trains ran into and reversed at the old terminus, at York.   The King Edward bridge and loop at Newcastle opened in 1906 shortened the through route by half a mile.   The Blyth & Tyne Railway, a Northumberland mineral line, dating to 1840, was absorbed in 1874.

A large part of the Newcastle suburban service was electrified in 1903.

Just before the grouping of the railways, the N.E.R. acquired the Hull & Barnsley line with a mileage of 66 and an extensive dock area at Hull.   Its main line extended from Hull to Cudworth, where it joined the Midland, in the neighbourhood of Barnsley, and was opened in 1885.   This company worked the new South Yorkshire Railway, opened in September, 1894, and it also had a branch line to Wath, opened in 1902.

North Road Works and Faverdale, Darlington, were the principal rolling stock shops of the N.E.R. and are still responsible for the making of many of the locomotives of the L. & N.E.R.

The G.N.R. formed the southern section in the east coast route to Scotland. The result of two rival schemes—the London and York and the Direct Northern, the Great Northern started with the opening of a local line from Grimsby to Louth, in 1848. In August, 1850, it reached Peterborough, and two years later the main line was opened from a temporary station at Maiden Lane (some distance north of the present King's Cross Station), through Grantham to Doncaster.

The opening of King's Cross Station, in October, 1852, completed the main line almost as it is to-day. York was then reached by running over the Lancashire & Yorkshire Railway from Askern to Knottingley, and thence over the York & North Midland line, from Burton Salmon. When built, King's Cross Station attracted a lot of attention, although it had then only an arrival and a departure platform. To-day it has 13 platforms, and, approximately, 500 trains use it every week-day. The engineering works for the first 25 miles out of London are particularly heavy ; there are nine tunnels (four having three parallel bores) on the main line, and one (Ponsbourne) on the loop line through Hertford, which, with its length of 2,686 yards, is the longest on the system. There is also the large Digswell viaduct at Welwyn, of 40 brick arches, each of 30ft. span. There are four large viaducts on the loop line—that at Hertford of 20 arches, and an intermediate steel girder span of $87\frac{1}{2}$ft. being the most important. Further north, on the main line at Peterborough, Newark and Doncaster there are fine examples of bridge work. At Peterboro' is a long viaduct which carries the line over the Oundle road, the old Great Eastern line and the River Nene ; the largest of these has a span of 220ft. The Newark Dyke Bridge, carrying the line over the Trent Navigation, has a single span of no less than $262\frac{1}{2}$ft. The Don Bridge at Doncaster has a span of 185ft.

For the first 100 miles out of London—that is, to the south end of Stoke tunnel—there is a four-track road practically all the way, with breaks at a few places. Unfortunately, some of these breaks occur near London ; the existence of five long tunnels, and the Welwyn viaduct, all fairly close together, made the work of widening too costly. For this reason, the loop line through Hertford to Stevenage was built to relieve the main line.

Apart from the main line of the East Coast route, the Great Northern had many feeder lines. Two local systems absorbed in 1865 were the West Yorkshire and the Leeds, Bradford & Halifax Railways, which enabled Leeds to be reached by running over other railways until the Doncaster & Wakefield Joint Line was completed in 1866. In the same year the Great Northern obtained access to Cambridge by joining up with the then Eastern Counties Railway at Shepreth. Other extensions stretched to Dewsbury and Keighley, and to Grimsby through Boston and Lincoln. Nottingham was reached over the Ambergate Railway from Grantham in 1852, and extended up the Erewash Valley as far as Pinxton in 1875. Another branch of this section from Kimberley to Egginton, in 1878, took the Great Northern through Ilkeston and Derby to Burton ; and, by the purchase of the small Stafford & Uttoxeter Railway, entered Stafford, the most westerly point reached by the Great Northern. A line to Leicester was opened in 1883, and at the same period several lines in Lincolnshire and Yorkshire. The Luton and St. Albans branches from Hatfield were opened in 1860 and 1865 respectively.

In the West Riding division are some very heavy constructional works. On the Halifax to Keighley line, there are Strine's cutting, 1,033 yards long, Queensbury tunnel, 2,501 yards long, followed by Thornton viaduct, formed of twenty 50ft. arches on an " S " curve ; and then Lees Moor tunnel, 1,533 yards long. The most notable Great Northern viaduct in Derbyshire is that across the Erewash Valley and the Midland Railway, near Ilkeston. There are sixteen 77ft. spans and three small ones, the total length being 1,449ft. and 63ft. above the ground. At Radcliffe, on the line to Nottingham, is a long viaduct over the Trent and the adjoining meadows. The eastern approach of 960ft. consists of 28 arches, whilst over the river itself are two brick arches and a single girder span. The Digby viaduct on the Pinxton branch is 1,718ft. long, and comprises 45 arches.

The locomotive works were originally at Boston, but they were moved to Doncaster soon after Mr. Patrick Stirling became locomotive superintendent in 1866. Doncaster is now the principal locomotive carriage and wagon building establishment of the L. & N.E.R.

The third large railway to form part of the L. & N.E.R. system was the Great Eastern. The section of 10½ miles from a temporary station at Devonshire Street to Romford marked the opening in 1839 of the Eastern Counties Railway. On July 1st a terminus at Bishopsgate was opened, and on the same date the line was extended to Brentwood. It was built on the 5ft. gauge, but converted a few years later to the 4ft. 8½in.

The line was taken as far as Colchester by the E.C.R. in 1843, while connection was made to Ipswich by the Eastern Union Railway. Another old portion of the G.E.R. was the London and Blackwall Ry., opened in 1840, and originally worked by rope-haulage. Its terminus was Fenchurch Street, which, since 1858, has also been the terminus of the London, Tilbury & Southend trains, and used for a time for the same purpose by the North London Railway.

The Cambridge line of the Great Eastern was built from Stratford to Newport by the Northern & Eastern, and opened as far as Bishop's Stortford in May, 1842. On January 1st, 1844, the Eastern Counties took over this line, and by combination with the Norfolk Railway, which owned the Norwich & Brandon and Norwich & Yarmouth Railways and by the completion of the line beyond Newport through Cambridge and Ely to Brandon, railway communication was completed between London and Norwich in July, 1845.

The completion of the Ipswich route to Norwich was carried out by the E.U.R., and opened to Norwich (Victoria) in November, 1849. Lowestoft was reached from Norwich in 1847.

A veritable network of small lines in East Anglia were formed into the combination known as the " Great Eastern Railway " when that title was adopted in 1862. The Great Eastern was actually an amalgamation of the Eastern Union, Eastern Counties, East Anglian, East Suffolk, and the Norfolk Railways. During the next 30 years many small additions were made to the system, and the " Essex Lines " were opened from Shenfield to Southminster and Southend in 1888-89.

The Great Eastern established steamer services from Harwich to the Continent, to Rotterdam (later to the Hook of Holland), and to Antwerp in 1876 ; and in 1883 these were transferred to Parkeston Quay. Just prior to the 1922 grouping, arrangements were made for the useful cross channel train-ferry service from Harwich to Zeebrugge.

The remaining railway to form the junior partner in the L. & N.E.R. was the Great Central. This originated in a cross-country line from Manchester to Sheffield, although it developed into one of the main routes between London, Sheffield and Manchester. The Great Central, as such, did not exist before August, 1897.

The nucleus of the system was the Sheffield, Ashton-under-Lyne and Manchester Railway, the first section to be used for passenger traffic from Manchester to Godley being opened in 1841. It was completed as far as the Woodhead tunnel, which is three miles long, early in 1845, and opened throughout six months later. On amalgamating with the lines connecting Sheffield with Grimsby and Lincoln, in 1847, the title was changed to the Manchester, Sheffield & Lincolnshire Railway. By leasing the old South Yorkshire Ry. in 1864, it obtained access to the colliery district around Barnsley. In partnership with the Great Northern and Midland Railways in the joint " Cheshire Lines " system, it obtained entry to Liverpool, and thus obtained a through route from the Mersey to the Humber, as well as access to Chester. Later—1905—it absorbed the Wrexham, Mold &

Connah's Quay Railway, which gave it access to Wrexham and an interest in the North Wales coalfield. Two years later it acquired the Lancashire, Derbyshire & East Coast Railway, which connected Chesterfield and the Derbyshire coalfields with Lincoln. Another line in the Nottingham colliery area forming part of this system was the Mansfield Railway, opened in 1916.

The M.S. & L.R. was the first railway to own docks, and the large fishing port of Grimsby owes its prosperity to its enterprise. It purchased an existing small dock about 1849. Subsequently, very large extensions were made, and a service of steamers to Hamburg, Rotterdam and Antwerp started.

A service of express trains between Manchester (London Road) and King's Cross was inaugurated in 1857, the M.S. & L.R. share of the work ending at Retford. On cutting the time to $4\frac{1}{2}$ hours, in 1883, the Retford stop was eliminated for the two best trains, and the M.S. & L. then worked the trains as far as Grantham. The following year another 15 minutes was cut off the running time.

In 1893 powers were obtained by the M.S. & L. for a new main line, 92 miles in length, from Annesley, passing through Nottingham, Leicester, Rugby and Aylesbury, to a junction with the Metropolitan Railway at Quainton Road. Arrangements were made to use the latter company's line to Harrow, whence additional tracks were laid to Finchley Road, and a new railway made to the Marylebone Terminus, London. The new route was opened for passenger traffic on March 15th, 1899. On this " London Extension," the principal works are the Bulwell viaduct of 26 arches ; three tunnels, a viaduct of 60 arches, a bridge over the Midland Station, and over the Trent at Nottingham ; the long viaduct through Leicester ; the bridge, 600ft. long, at Rugby, over the L.M. & S. ; Catesby tunnel, 1 mile 1,237 yards in length, and the Brackley viaduct.

Two years before the opening of the London Extension, the M.S. & L.R. had adopted the title of the Great Central.

4-6-0 TYPE EXPRESS PASSENGER LOCOMOTIVE, "CASTLE" CLASS, GREAT WESTERN RAILWAY.

Four cylinders, 16in. diameter by 26in. stroke ; driving wheels, 6ft. 8½in. diameter ; boiler pressure, 225 lbs. per sq. in. ; tractive effort, 31,625 lbs. These are the main particulars of the very successful class of standard express engines of the Great Western Railway, introduced in 1923, and built at Swindon Works. They are named after famous castles adjacent to that line. Length over buffers, 65ft. 2in. Water capacity of tender, 4,000 gallons. Weight, in working order, engine and tender, 119 tons 17 cwts. One of these engines usually hauls the *Cheltenham Flyer*, Swindon to Paddington, 77¼ miles, in 65 minutes, the fastest booked train in the country. No. 4073, *Caerphilly Castle*, was shown at the Wembley Exhibition of 1925. It was No. 5006, *Tregenna Castle*, that ran 39 miles at an average speed of 90 miles an hour, with the *Cheltenham Flyer* on June 26th, 1932.

HIGH-PRESSURE COMPOUND LOCOMOTIVE, No. 10,000, LONDON & NORTH EASTERN RAILWAY.

The special feature of this 4-6-4 high-pressure, four-cylinder, compound locomotive is the water tube boiler, which carries a working-pressure of 450 lbs. per sq. inch. This was jointly patented by Mr. H. N. Gresley, of the L. & N.E. Railway, and Mr. H. E. Yarrow. The boiler was built at the Works of Messrs. Yarrow & Co., Ltd., and the mechanical part of the locomotive at Darlington Works.

The two high-pressure inside cylinders, 10in. by 26in. drive the front coupled axle, and the two low-pressure outside 20in. by 26in. drive the second axle. At starting, steam limited to 200 lbs. pressure can be admitted to the low-pressure pair of cylinders. The coupled wheels are 6ft. 8in. diameter, and the carrying wheels, front and rear, 3ft. 2in. diameter.

The boiler has one top steam drum, 3ft. diameter and 28ft. long, the firebox being formed of banks of tubes passing downwards to two lower water drums, 18in. diameter and 11ft. long. The front part is formed of further tubes passing to two water drums, 19in. diameter by 13ft. 6in. long, placed at a higher level than the others. A superheater is fitted in the front end of the main flue. As the top of the boiler is carried up to the limit allowed by the construction gauge, no chimney can be allowed to project above it, and this detail is concealed, except in a front view.

CONVERTED 4-6-0 EXPRESS LOCOMOTIVE, No. 2329, "STEPHENSON," SOUTHERN RAILWAY.

Seven express tank locomotives of the 4-6-4 type were built between 1914 and 1922 at the Brighton Works of the former London, Brighton & South Coast Railway, and used on the fast trains between London and Brighton and Eastbourne.

Consequent upon the electrification of these sections of the Southern Railway, and no suitable work remaining for them owing to their limited coal and water capacity, they are being converted into 4-6-0 type tender engines at Eastleigh Works. The first to be completed is No. 2329, *Stephenson*.

The rebuilding of the engines, raising of the boiler pressure to 180 lbs. per sq. in., and provision of a standard 5,000 gallons bogie tender makes them of general utility. Opportunity is being made to name these engines after locomotive engineers of the past, except one, *Remembrance*, No. 2333, chosen as the War Memorial locomotive of the L.B. & S.C. Railway, and also the last locomotive built at Brighton Works for that line.

REPLICA OF THE "ROCKET" LOCOMOTIVE OF 1829. (*Photo: Robt. Stephenson & Co., Ltd.*)

As nearly as possible, an exact replica, in all details, of the *Rocket*, which took part in the Rainhill trials in October, 1829, has been constructed by Robert Stephenson & Co., Ltd., for the Science Museum, South Kensington. It is a reproduction of the original, both in design and materials, as nearly as possible as it was on the opening day of the Liverpool & Manchester Railway trials. Some of the details have been settled from contemporary sketches made by John Rastrick, which he used at the trials, particularly in regard to the firebox. The boiler is of iron plates, ½in. thick, riveted together by hand with wrought-iron rivets. The driving wheels are built up of wood spokes with cast-iron centres ; the tyres are of wrought-iron. The other wheels are of cast-iron.

It will be remembered that at the Rainhill trials, the *Rocket* was the only engine which not only complied with the conditions, but also performed the duties imposed without material failure of any kind, a feat which is still regarded as a remarkable performance, and so won the £500 prize, and became the prototype for the engines subsequently ordered by the Liverpool & Manchester Railway.

Beside the chimney will be noticed the mercury pressure-gauge, indicating the pressure from 45 to 50 lbs. per sq. in., although arrangements had been made for mounting a dial gauge as well.

Considerable doubt exists as to the design of the original firebox of the *Rocket*, but Rastrick's sketches show a box formed of two copper plates, pinched together all round and dished to form a 3in. water space between them at the top and sides, and riveted and tied at the bottom by four stays on which the firebars rest. The iron front and back plates have no water space. The engine was fired by coke. The firebox water space was connected with the boiler barrel by pipes at the top and bottom. The working steam pressure was 50 lbs. per sq. in.

Two safety-valves were provided, one loaded by a weighted lever and the other by springs. The exhaust steam passed into the chimney, which was 15ft. high, by two pipes fitted with nozzles.

Its two cylinders, fastened to plates on the boiler, and inclined downward at an angle of 35°, drive crank pins on the front wheels. The cylinders are 8in. diameter by 17in. stroke, and the driving wheels 4ft. 8½in. diameter. The trailing wheels are 30in. diameter, and the wheelbase 7ft. 2in. Total heating surface 134 sq. ft. Grate area, 6 sq. ft. Weight of engine, in working order, about 4¼ tons. Tractive force of engine, 960 lbs.

F

The large docks at Immingham, on the south bank of the Humber, were opened in 1912. The extensive marshalling yard, at Wath, was built in 1907, to deal with 7,000 wagons a day.

North of the Border the main constituent of the L. & N.E.R. was the North British Railway, the largest railway in Scotland. The oldest part, the Monkland & Kirkintilloch Railway, was opened in 1826, and the first locomotives built in Scotland were two built for this line by Murdoch and Aitken, to the designs of J. Dodds, in 1832. They were of the Stephenson " Killingworth " type. Two other small lines which became part of the North British after 1840 were the Ballochney Railway, closely associated with the Monkland line, and the Edinburgh and Dalkeith.

The North British itself was begun in the line between Edinburgh and Berwick, opened in 1846, making a link in the chain of the East Coast route from London to Aberdeen. In 1862 it was amalgamated with the Edinburgh, Perth & Dundee Railway, the Edinburgh, Leith & Granton Railway, and the Forth Ferry ; and in 1865 with the Edinburgh & Glasgow Railway. The latter had been opened in 1842, and was the means of bringing North British influence into the West of Scotland. To the south of Edinburgh, an extension towards Carlisle was opened as far as Hawick in 1849. This line, known as the " Waverley route," was taken through Carlisle, and terminated at Silloth, on the Solway Firth ; it was opened in 1862. A feeder from Riccarton Junction went to join the N.E.R. at Morpeth and Hexham. By amalgamation, and opening new lines, the North British obtained a monopoly of railway transport in the coalfields of the county of Fife. In its final form, when it became part of the L. & N.E.R., the North British was composed of more than fifty different companies added to the original one.

In the early days communication from Edinburgh to the north was by train to Granton, thence by steam ferry to Burntisland, where the Fife trains were joined. Merchandise traffic was transported in goods steamers provided with rails on to which the wagons were run direct, a communicating cradle being lowered on to the deck and pier to allow of this being done. The wagons were hauled on and off by rope. The ferry is still in use, and serves as a short cut across the Forth for motorists.

The Forth Bridge, which made rapid transport possible, was not opened until 1890. This masterpiece of bridge building occupied seven years in construction, and cost $2\frac{1}{2}$ millions.

Passengers and goods for Dundee and beyond were conveyed by steamer across the Firth of Tay from Tayport to Broughty Ferry. The ill-fated Tay Bridge, designed to improve this passage, was opened in June, 1878, and wrecked in the storm of December 29th, 1879, when a train fell into the Tay, with great loss of life. The present Tay Bridge was opened for traffic in 1887.

The West Highland Railway—140 miles long—was the most recent extension of importance to the N.B.R. It was opened to Fort William in 1894. It leaves the line which serves the north bank of the Clyde, at Craigendoran, and by a single track with heavy grades skirts Loch Lomond, crosses Rannoch Moor, where it reaches a height of 1,350ft., and then descends to sea-level at Fort William. Thence it is continued to Mallaig, opened in 1901. On it some of the finest scenery in the British Isles can be seen.

Mention must be made of the fine Edinburgh (Waverley) Station, the biggest in Scotland. Built for through running, with terminal bays for suburban traffic, it has nine platforms, and covers 18 acres. At Queen Street Station, Glasgow, trains were assisted by a steel rope up the gradient of 1 in 45 to Cowlairs. The rope haulage was discarded in 1912, and all trains beyond one engine's power are now assisted by a pusher, which, on expresses, is slipped.

The only other railway to form part of the L. & N.E.R. to be mentioned was the Great North of Scotland. This connected Aberdeen with Elgin, with branches to Peterhead, Fraserburgh, Macduff,

Banff, and Boat of Garten, while a southern branch traversed the valley of the Dee from Aberdeen to Ballater. It is nearly all single track. Apart from its heavy tourist traffic, in the summer, the fish and livestock traffic accounted for the bulk of its revenue. The first portion of the G.N.S.R. was from Kittybrewster, on the northern outskirts of Aberdeen, to Huntly, and opened in September, 1854. There are few extensive engineering works on this line, the largest being the Fochabers viaduct, over the River Spey, near its mouth. This consists of seven spans, with a total length of 950ft., the principal span having a length of 350ft.

CHAPTER IX

GREAT WESTERN RAILWAY

AMID the general changing under the grouping of the railways in 1923, the Great Western was the only one to proudly maintain its original title and identity. The principal lines taken over to form the Great Western system of to-day were the Cambrian Railways, the Taff Vale, Barry, Rhymney and Brecon & Merthyr Railways, Alexandra (Newport & South Wales) Docks and Railway, Cardiff, Rhondda and Swansea Bay, Port Talbot, Burry Port & Gwendraeth Valley, and the Midland & South Western Junction Railways, as well as a number of small companies.

The system now comprises 9,075 miles of single track and a route mileage of 3,795, with about 1,500 stations and halts, while it owns 3,608 steam locomotives, 17 rail motors, 20 electric and 4 Diesel vehicles, 6,142 carriages and 80,350 merchandise and mineral wagons, also 14 steamers.

As mentioned in Chapter I, the original main line of the G.W.R. was constructed by Isambard Kingdom Brunel, on the 7ft. gauge, and connected London with Bristol, via Bath, a distance of 118¼ miles. It was completed in 1841.

When Brunel laid out the line to Bristol for high speed, the difficulties of construction were aggravated by the lack of experience on the part of his assistants. On the first section out of London, the chief engineering undertakings were the viaduct crossing the Brent Valley, the Maidenhead bridge over the Thames, and the cutting through the high ground between Twyford and Sonning.

The line as far as Taplow was opened on June 4th, 1838, to Reading, March 31st, 1840, Steventon on June 1st, Farringdon Road (now named Challow) on July 20th, and Hay Lane, near Wootton Bassett, on December 16th of the same year.

At the Bristol end, the section as far as Bath, which included several tunnels, was opened on June 20th, 1840, so that only about 24 miles remained unfinished. This length, however, included the Box tunnel, 1 mile 7 furlongs in length.

By May 31st, 1841, trains were running from London to Chippenham, and on June 30th to Bristol.

The original G.W.R. ended at Bristol, but by associating itself with the Bristol & Exeter Railway, the South Devon Railway from Exeter to Plymouth, the Cornwall Railway, connecting Plymouth with Truro and Falmouth, and the West Cornwall Railway from Truro to Penzance, the main line extended as far westward as a railway could be carried—326½ miles from Paddington.

The first half of the B. & E.R. to Taunton was opened on June 14th, 1841, so that, on completion of the Great Western, passengers were able to travel considerably further west than Bristol. Beyond Taunton, high ground has to be crossed, and there is a steady rise for 12 miles, finishing in a grade of 1 in 85 to the Whiteball tunnel, five furlongs long. The line then descends, with lengths of up grade here and there, to Exeter. The 75 miles from Bristol to Exeter were opened throughout in 1844.

F 2

Brunel also acted as engineer for the S.D.R. route from Exeter to Plymouth—a very difficult railway to construct throughout. Leaving Exeter, the right bank of the Exe is followed to Starcross, and then the seashore, past Dawlish to Teignmouth. Beyond this point the left bank of the Teign is taken, until it is crossed just before reaching Newton Abbot. So far the line is practically level, but beyond it crosses difficult country. Between Newton Abbot and Totnes, Dainton tunnel summit has to be passed, and this involves gradients of 1 in 57 and 1 in 36. West of Totnes, there is the stiff Rattery Bank, the steepest part of which is 1 in 46, while the up east-bound trains have to climb the two miles Hemerdon Bank, near Plympton, on a gradient of 1 in 43.

It is interesting to note that the Exeter-Newton Abbot section was worked on the atmospheric system from November, 1847, to 1849.

In 1848 the line was opened to Plymouth, and the same year saw the completion of the Torquay branch.

The extension westwards, Plymouth to Truro, was the broad-gauge Cornwall Railway through very heavy country, and a notable feature is the number of viaducts on this section. There are 34 of these, and, when first constructed, timber was largely employed.

The last stretch of the western main line was the West Cornwall Railway, from Truro to Penzance, through Redruth. This had been built to the standard gauge as the successor of a mineral railway between Redruth and Hayle, opened in 1841, which included two rope-worked inclines. This line was extended westwards to Penzance in 1851, and to Truro in the following year. On the completion of the Cornwall Railway, in 1859, a third rail was laid down to enable the broad-gauge rolling stock to run through to Penzance. South Devon Railway engines began working into Penzance in 1860.

The Great Western also owns many branch lines in Cornwall, several having been built by small local companies. The Liskeard & Looe, and the Cornwall Minerals, between Fowey and Newquay, are typical of these. Other branches are to Falmouth, Launceston, Bodmin, Helston and St. Ives. When completed, and until May, 1892, the whole of the main line was laid to a gauge of 7ft., although an extra rail for narrow gauge traffic was in use as far as Exeter, and, as above mentioned, on the extreme westerly portion.

The inconvenience and expense of working the railway with two gauges made it imperative to abolish the broad-gauge track. Various sections were dealt with from time to time, and the final conversion to standard gauge took place in 1892. The feat of converting 177 miles, comprising branches in Devon and Cornwall and the main line from Exeter to Truro, was accomplished in two days. The last broad-gauge passenger train to leave Paddington was the 5 p.m. to Plymouth, on Friday, May 20th. The very last broad-gauge train to run was the up " Cornishman," which left Penzance at 9 p.m. on that day. The whole of the conversion occupied only 30 hours, and on Monday, May 23rd, the usual service of trains was in operation on the standard gauge rails.

The second main route is that diverging at Swindon via Gloucester, and thence south-west and west to Cardiff and South Wales. The line from Gloucester to New Milford—opened throughout in 1856—was built by the South Wales Railway, and taken over by the G.W.R. in 1863, although it had always been worked by them. It was constructed on the broad gauge by Brunel, and the chief engineering works were the bridges over the Severn, at Gloucester, over the Wye at Chepstow, and over the Usk, near Newport, the Landore viaduct, one-third of a mile long, and the Cockett tunnel, near Swansea, of about the same length. Of these the Chepstow tubular bridge was the most difficult work. This has three spans of 100ft. each, and one of 290ft., making the total length, with the piers, of 610ft.

The third main line of the Great Western leaves the original Bristol route at Didcot and runs north through Oxford, Leamington and Warwick to Birmingham (Snow Hill). It then continues north-ward through the Black Country, Wolverhampton and Shrewsbury, and traverses the famous Vale of Llangollen to Chester, finally reaching Birkenhead over the Joint London, Midland & Scottish and Great Western line.

Until the middle 'fifties the G.W.R. was essentially a broad-gauge line, extending as far north as Wolverhampton, through Oxford and Birmingham. North of this point the Shrewsbury & Birmingham and Shrewsbury & Chester Railways were of standard gauge, and early in the 'fifties a fight for their possession ensued between the G.W. and L. & N.W.R. This ended in a victory for the former as regards ownership, but conditional on their remaining of standard gauge.

Until 1886, when the Severn Tunnel was opened, all G.W.R. traffic between South Wales and London and Bristol had to be worked via Gloucester and Swindon. There certainly was a steamer ferry introduced in 1863 between New Passage, on the Gloucestershire shore, and Portskewett. The Severn & Wye Railway bridge, opened in 1879, between Sharpness and Lydney, was the only way of crossing the Severn below Gloucester, except by the local ferries. But this bridge was of little use for through traffic, as it had no connection with the Swindon-Gloucester line of the G.W.R., and the junction with the M.R. at Berkeley Road went towards Gloucester. More-over, it had only a single track. Work was commenced on the Severn tunnel in 1873. Water broke into the workings in 1879, causing considerable delay in completion. The first train to pass through on January 9th, 1886, was a coal train from Aberdare to Southampton, and on December 1st of the same year the passenger service was started. The length of the tunnel is four miles, 624 yards, of which $2\frac{3}{4}$ miles is below the river bed. The tunnel is kept dry by Cornish beam engines, with 70in. cylinders, and pumping 75 million gallons of water per week.

Of late years the Great Western has carried out a number of extensive schemes for reducing the main line journeys, by new lines forming short cuts across angles. The first of these was the South Wales & Bristol Direct Railway, via Badminton, 33 miles in length, in 1903, and its extension to Avonmouth in 1910. This line leaves the main line at Wootton Bassett and joins the old South Wales line to Cardiff at Severn Tunnel Junction, while the Bristol connection was made at Filton. By this route the distance between London and Bristol was reduced to 117 miles 55 chains.

By re-alignment and doubling the Berks and Hants line, and a new short line from Patney and Chirton to the old route, via Chippenham, at Westbury, the Weymouth service was diverted via Newbury, and the distance to the port shortened by 14 miles. The new route was opened in 1901. By the completion of the Castle Cary to Langport line, opened July 1st, 1906, the distance between London and Taunton and places west of the latter was shortened by nearly 19 miles, and the West of England expresses were diverted to this route.

The Acton and Northolt line, opened 1903, the Northolt to Ashendon line in 1905-06, Joint Great Western and Great Central, and the Ashendon-Aynho in 1910 gave the Great Western the shortest route between London and Birmingham, reducing the distance by the old route via Oxford from 129 miles to 110 miles 47 chains, with a corresponding reduction to places north of Banbury.

The Cheltenham & Honeybourne line opened in 1904-06, and the Birmingham & North Warwickshire line, completed in 1907, enabled a new cross country service from Birmingham to Bristol, via Stratford-on-Avon, to be inaugurated.

Another great enterprise of the G.W.R. was the construction of Fishguard Harbour, on the north coast of Pembrokeshire, together with the railway connection thereto. This was a revival of a scheme dating back to 1845, when Brunel recognized Fishguard as the most suitable point for the South of Ireland and Transatlantic traffic. This new route to the south of Ireland, via Fishguard and Rosslare, was inaugurated on August 30th, 1906. The distance from London to the Welsh port is 262 miles.

Among the constituents of the G.W.R. group were the erstwhile Cambrian Railways and the Taff Vale Railway. The former served mid-Wales, with a main line from Whitchurch on the L.M.S.R. through Oswestry, Welshpool, Montgomery, Machynlleth and Barmouth, to Pwllheli, with branches taking off at Moat Lane Junction to Brecon, and from Dovey Junction to Aberystwyth. It had but a single track for all except 27 of its 242 miles. The largest engineering feature is the Barmouth viaduct, 800 yards long, in 113 spans, crossing the estuary of the River Mawddach. For most of its length this viaduct is constructed of wood, but there is a steel swing bridge at its northern end. There is also a very deep cutting at Talerddig, on the main line between Moat Lane and Machynlleth. The main asset of the Cambrian was the tourist traffic, its territory being a favourite holiday ground for pleasure seekers. Connection with the G.W.R. is made at Oswestry and at Welshpool.

The Taff Vale Railway traversed a densely populated country, and carried an enormous mineral traffic. There are two to six tracks on much of the main route between Merthyr and Cardiff, and four tracks as far as Porth, on the Rhondda Valley line. It was opened between Cardiff and Merthyr before the G.W.R. was completed to Bristol.

The Barry Railway dated from 1884, built docks for the shipment of coal at Barry Island, and also constructed railways to the Rhondda Valley, and through the Vale of Glamorgan to Bridgend. The Rhymney Railway had a main line through the colliery district from Cardiff northwards to Nantybwch, where it joined the L. & N.W.R. section of the L.M. & S.R. One of its branches also served the Aberdare Valley.

Another South Wales line was the Brecon & Merthyr. Originally a line connecting the towns of Brecon and Merthyr, on which occurs the famous Tal y Bont incline, some 7 miles in length, mostly at 1 in 37 and 38, it was extended to form a connection with the G.W.R. at Bassaleg, near Newport.

Other South Wales mineral lines taken over were the Cardiff Railway, Rhondda & Swansea Bay, Neath & Brecon, Port Talbot Railway & Docks and Burry Port & Gwendraeth Valley Railways. Another small railway taken over was the Cleobury Mortimer & Ditton Priors Light Railway.

The Midland & South Western Junction Railway provided a direct route from Cheltenham and the Midlands via Andover to Southampton.

It is the claim of the G.W.R. to have carried members of the reigning house more frequently than any other British railway. The first journey made by His Majesty King George V was nearly 70 years ago when, but a few months old, he was taken from Paddington to Windsor. Since then his journeys have taken him to many parts of the system. Among these was his visit to Bristol in 1902 to cut the first sod of the Royal Edward Dock. On May 25th, 1903, as Prince of Wales and President of the Royal Agricultural Society, he travelled by the first train carrying passengers over the newly constructed line between Old Oak Common and Park Royal, where a new station had been built specially for the Royal Show. A brass plate commemorating this event was fixed on either side of the station premises which " His Royal Highness was pleased to name ' Park Royal.' "

In July, 1903, Their Majesties, then Prince and Princess of Wales, paid a visit to Cornwall. A special train was put on for their non-stop journey to Plymouth via Bristol, a distance of $245\frac{3}{4}$ miles in four hours, and as a result of the success of this run, the famous " Cornish Riviera Express " came into being.

On the occasion of Their Majesties' wedding two passenger

locomotives were named after them, No. 1128, *Duke of York*, and No. 1129, *Princess May*, and after the Coronation, the first four-cylinder express passenger engine, built at Swindon in 1910, was named *Queen Mary*. This locomotive is still in service.

In 1927, when the Company introduced the " King " class locomotives, the first was named *King George V*. It was this engine which was sent to America in the same year and exhibited at the Fair of the Iron Horse, organized by the Baltimore & Ohio Railroad.

CHAPTER X

SOUTHERN RAILWAY

THE three railways which formed the Southern Railway group were the London & South Western, London, Brighton & South Coast, and South Eastern & Chatham Railways. They are all mainly passenger lines, and have a very large short distance traffic. The whole of the district south-east, south and south-west of the metropolis is thickly populated by people who have to travel to and from town, and the suburban traffic dealt with morning and evening is far and away the most concentrated and difficult to work in the British Isles. On the South Eastern section there are four London termini, just north of the Thames : Cannon Street, Holborn Viaduct, Charing Cross and Victoria. The Brighton section has Victoria and London Bridge, while the South Western has Waterloo.

Possessing the shortest sea routes, the S.R. occupies the leading position as carriers between England and the Continent. In addition to the sailings from Dover and Folkestone to Ostend, Calais and Boulogne, services are also maintained between Newhaven and Dieppe, and from Southampton to Havre, St. Malo, Caen and Cherbourg, as well as to the Channel Islands. To operate these services it has a fleet of about 40 steamships.

Electric traction, first brought into use on the South Western section in the London area in 1915, has now been adopted on all the London suburban lines, as far as Sevenoaks, Dorking, Guildford and Windsor, as well as the main lines to Brighton, Worthing, Eastbourne and Hastings. The route mileage of electrical working of the S.R. is 447, and the track mileage, 1,160. The total route mileage is now 2,170, and it owns 2,044 steam locomotives, 8,032 coaching vehicles, 34,458 wagons, and 1,629 vehicles for electric working.

Although the Western section of the S.R. reaches as far west as Padstow, on the Cornish coast—$259\frac{3}{4}$ miles from Waterloo—the main line proper of the former L. & S.W.R. runs in an entirely different direction, and for 79 miles only, Southampton being the objective. In fact, the system was originally known as the London & Southampton Railway, and, with the exception of the London & Birmingham Railway, was the oldest of the main trunk lines out of the Metropolis, the opening from the Nine Elms passenger terminus as far as Woking occurring in May, 1838. Through rail communication was effected between London and Southampton in May, 1840. A year previously, a change of title to that of the L. & S.W.R. indicated a determination to extend the system further afield. How the L. & S.W. extended the narrow gauge into the west of England is an interesting story, but too lengthy to be related here.

It was soon realized that Nine Elms was inconvenient as the London terminus, and a three miles extension to Waterloo was opened in 1848, and Nine Elms became the London goods depot. In 1854 the railway was extended from Basingstoke to Andover, and in May, 1857, to Salisbury. In the same year Weymouth was reached by running over the G.W.R. from Dorchester, and in January, 1859, Portsmouth was brought into touch with Waterloo by the opening of the " Direct " line from Guildford, through Haslemere and Havant.

The line to Reading had been opened in 1856. Exeter was reached in 1860 by an extension west of Salisbury, through Sherborne and Yeovil ; the distance from Waterloo being 171¾ miles, or 22 miles shorter than the G.W.R. route, though the opening of the shorter route by that company in 1906 reduced the advantage by the S.R. to one of two miles only.

Not for long was Exeter the Western terminus, for in 1862 a lease was taken of the broad gauge lines to Crediton and Barnstaple from a junction with the Bristol & Exeter Railway at Cowley Bridge. An extension was made from Exeter (Central) to the G.W.R. St. David's Station, and the gauge " mixed " thence to Bideford. Yeoford Junction, on this North Devon line, was the starting point of a new line, opened as far as Okehampton in 1867, which eventually reached both Plymouth and Padstow.

Bournemouth was linked up with Waterloo in 1870 via Ringwood and Christchurch. The Bideford line was extended to Torrington in 1872, and two years later branches were opened from Barnstaple to Ilfracombe, and to Sidmouth. By the acquisition jointly with the Midland Railway of the Somerset & Dorset Railway, in 1875, the L. & S.W.R. obtained a connection with the Midland, at Bath. As successors of the Somerset Central and Dorset Central Railways, the Somerset & Dorset line extended from Wimborne, on the L. & S.W.R. to Burnham-on-Sea. There was a branch from Glastonbury to Wells, and an extension from Evercreech to Bath. Connection of the S. & D.R. with the S.R. main line is effected at Templecombe. There is considerable traffic over the S. & D. line between Bournemouth and the Midlands and North, especially during the summer months.

The L. & S.W.R. originally reached Plymouth over the G.W.R. from Lydford by a mixed gauge line through Tavistock and Yelverton, but in 1890 an alternative route extending from Lydford through Devonport to Plymouth was opened. Two years later their Friary terminus on the east side of Plymouth was opened, 230½ miles from Waterloo.

In March, 1888, the distance from Waterloo to Bournemouth was reduced from 116 to 108 miles, by the direct line through the New Forest from Brockenhurst to Christchurch.

Further extensions to North Cornwall were made from Oke-hampton, first to Holsworthy (1879), to Launceston and to Camel-ford (1893), then to Bude from Holsworthy (1898), and to Padstow from Wadebridge (in 1899). More recently a line across country between Torrington and Halwill has been completed by the S.R.

The growth of trade at Southampton since the Company took over the Docks in 1892 has been enormous.

Among improvements of recent years, the rebuilding and re-modelling of Waterloo Station should be mentioned, also the opening of a large freight marshalling yard at Feltham. The rebuilding of Waterloo occupied many years, and was finally completed in 1922. With its 21 platforms, the station now ranks as the largest and finest in the country. The marshalling yard at Feltham, opened in 1921, is operated on the " hump " principle, and it incorporates all the best features of a modern shunting yard of this type.

Among the several small railways of the Southern group, the three systems of the Isle of Wight are of interest. The Isle of Wight Railway, running from St. John's Road, Ryde, was opened to Ventnor in 1866 ; on this line is a tunnel at Ventnor, 1,276 yards long. The earliest line on the island, however, was the Newport & Cowes, opened in 1862, while thirteen years later the Ryde & Newport and a line to Sandown were opened. These three lines amalgamated to form the Isle of Wight Central Railway, which also took over the working of the Freshwater, Yarmouth & Newport Railway from its opening, in 1889 until 1913, when the latter commenced to provide its own rolling stock. The I. of W.C. also worked a branch to Ventnor in 1900, in competition with the I. of W.R. The I. of W.R. had a

4-8-2 FOUR-CYLINDER COMPOUND EXPRESS LOCOMOTIVE, No. 41,001, EASTERN RAILWAY OF FRANCE.

During the past ten years, great improvements have been made in locomotive design on the French Railways. The heaviest trains between Paris and Nancy and Strasbourg are hauled by these " Mountain " type locomotive, the loads ranging up to 510 tons on a far from easy road. The coupled wheels have a diameter of 6ft. 5in. The high-pressure cylinders, which are outside the frames, have a diameter 17¾in. and a stroke of 28¼in. The inside low pressure cylinders have the same piston stroke, but a diameter of 26in. They are worked by separate sets of Walschaert valve gear. The boiler pressure is 250 lbs. per sq. inch. The weight of engine and tender in running trim is a little over 185 tons.

HIGH-PRESSURE " PACIFIC " OR 4-6-2 TYPE COMPOUND EXPRESS LOCOMOTIVE, SERIES 04, GERMAN STATE RAILWAYS.

The latest development in locomotive practice on the German Railways has been in the use of higher steam pressures and temperatures. The four-cylinder compound classified as Series 04 has a pressure of 355 lbs. per sq. in. and a superheat temperature of 420°C. The high-pressure cylinders are 13¾in. diameter, and the low-pressure 20½in., with a common stroke of 26in. The coupled wheels are 6ft. 6¾in. diameter. In working order the engine alone weighs 104 tons. The tractive effort is approximately 20,000 lbs.

TWO-CYLINDER 2-8-2, OR " MIKADO," TYPE LOCOMOTIVE, No. 5501, BELGIAN NATIONAL RAILWAYS.

For passenger service on the Luxemburg line. The section between Brussels and Arlon—121 miles in length—has many heavy gradients, with lengths of 7½ and 9⅛ miles as steep as 1 in 66 to 1 in 62. The two cylinders have a diameter of 28¾in., with a piston stroke also of 28¾in., with Walschaert valve gear. The diameter of the coupled wheels is 5ft. 7in. The total weight is 131 tons in working order.

2-10-4 BOOSTER-FITTED LOCOMOTIVE, No. 10,000 FOR THE RUSSIAN SOVIET RAILWAYS.

Built in the United States, several of these large and powerful locomotives have been put into service on hauling coal trains from the Donetz district to Moscow, and are to suit the Russian 5ft. gauge track. The ten-coupled wheels are 5ft. in diameter. The cylinders are 27½in. diameter by 30in. stroke. The boiler, which carries a working pressure of 241 lbs. per sq. inch, is 6ft. 8in. diameter. Tractive effort is 61,610 lbs., while the booster on the tender gives an additional 13,224 lbs.

4–8–4 FOUR-CYLINDER EXPRESS GOODS TANK LOCOMOTIVE, No. 6303, NETHERLANDS RAILWAYS.

For dealing with the coal traffic from the mines in South Limburg, a powerful type of goods engine has been introduced for fairly high speed. The driving wheels are 5ft. 1in. diameter, and four cylinders are used ; these are 16½in. diameter by 26in. stroke. The working pressure is 199 lbs. per sq. in., and the tractive effort is estimated at 32,340 lbs. Total weight in running order, 126¼ tons.

4–8–2, OR " MOUNTAIN " TYPE LOCOMOTIVE, No. 1773, MADRID, ZARAGOZA AND ALICANTE RAILWAY, SPAIN.

There are now seventy-five of these engines working practically all express trains leaving and arriving at Madrid. These engines have two cylinders, 24½in. diameter by 28in. stroke, with poppet valves and coupled wheels, 5ft. 8⅞in. diameter. The working pressure is 200 lbs. per sq. inch, and the tractive effort 32,000 lbs. These engines were built by the large and important Maquinista Terrestre y Maritima Works, at St. Audries, a suburb of Barcelona. The total weight of the engine alone is 104 tons in service.

" MIKADO " TYPE LOCOMOTIVE, PEIPING LIAO-NING RAILWAY, CHINA.

Modern Chinese steam locomotives have a distinctive style, but many characteristics have been taken from British and American practice. It is now standard practice to fit the locomotives throughout China with the air brake and central automatic couplers. The " Mikado " type engine shown was built by the North British Locomotive Co., of Glasgow, to suit the standard 4ft. 8½in. gauge. It has cylinders 21in. diameter by 28in. stroke, with coupled wheels 4ft. 6in. diameter. A mechanical stoker, with a stoker engine, forms part of the equipment, with a rocking grate. Other refinements include a tube cleaner, electric lighting equipment, pneumatic sanding gear, speed recorder, pyrometer, etc. The engine weighs 84¼ tons when ready for the road, while the bogie tender, full, weighs just under 60 tons.

4–8–2 THREE-CYLINDER PASSENGER LOCOMOTIVE, CZECHO-SLOVAKIAN STATE RAILWAYS.

The heavy grades of the main routes of the railways of Czecho-Slovakia call for a locomotive with high tractive effort and rapid acceleration rather than speed capacity, and the example illustrated has been built by the Skoda Company for express passenger service and fast goods.

Although four axles are coupled, the rigid wheelbase is only 19ft. The coupled wheels are 6ft. in diameter, and the leading bogie wheels, 2ft. 10¾in. diameter, while the trailing wheels are 4ft. 3⅝in. diameter. The two outside cylinders are horizontal, whilst the inside one is inclined 1 in 10 ; all are 21⅝in. diameter by 26¾in. stroke. The boiler, 6ft. in external diameter, carries a working pressure of 227 lbs. A superheater affords 968.7 sq. ft. of heating surface, and this, with 2,529.6 sq. ft. evaporative surface and 213.5 sq. ft. of the firebox and arch tubes, gives a combined total of 3711.6 sq. ft. The grate area is 52 sq. ft. The engine weighs 102 tons, in working order.

G

branch from Brading to Bembridge.   The extension from St. John's Road, Ryde, to the Pier Head, at Ryde, was made jointly by the South Western and Brighton Railways in 1880.

What is now the Central section of the S.R. was the London, Brighton & South Coast Railway, its various lines occupying the territory between London, Hastings and Portsmouth.   Its direct route between London and Brighton had a branch from Keymer Junction serving Lewes, Eastbourne, Hastings, and its Continental port of Newhaven.   There is the line to Portsmouth via Epsom, Horsham, Ford Junction and Chichester, and other routes are to Tonbridge via Oxted, and to East Grinstead, also there is the coast line from Hastings via Brighton and Worthing to Portsmouth.

When Parliament, in 1839, sanctioned the making of the London & Brighton and South Eastern Railways, it was on the understanding that they should form a continuation of the London & Croydon Railway, southwards, and between Norwood and Redhill should use the line jointly.   At Norwood the Brighton line commenced and ran due south to the coast ; it was opened throughout, from London Bridge to Brighton, on September 21st, 1841.   Meanwhile, the Brighton and Shoreham section had been in use since May, 1840 ; it was extended to Worthing, and thence to Chichester and Portsmouth in 1847.   Eastwards the line reached St. Leonards in 1846.   The L. & B. and L. & C.R. amalgamated in 1846, and adopted the title " London, Brighton & South Coast Railway."   In succeeding years the system was extended by various cross-country connecting lines, and by many developments in the London suburban area. Entrance to the West End of London was obtained through Clapham and Battersea, the terminus at Victoria being opened in October, 1860.

The section avoiding Redhill Station, opened in 1900, extends for six miles from Stoats Nest to Earlswood.   There are four long tunnels on the main line, viz. Merstham Old and New (the latter on the avoiding line) ; Balcombe and Clayton, measuring 1,832, 2,113, 1,113 and 2,266 yards respectively. North of Oxted, on the line from Croydon, is another tunnel of 2,266 yards. There are also deep cuttings at Merstham, and approaching Brighton. Another large work is the viaduct across the Ouse valley, between Balcombe and Haywards Heath. With a length of 1,475ft. and a maximum height of 90ft., the viaduct is formed of 37 arches, each with a span of 30ft. In Brighton there are two other viaducts, that over the London Road, on the Lewes line, and the Lewes Road viaduct on the Kemp Town branch. Modern developments include the rebuilding of Victoria Station in 1908. Electric traction on the overhead system was inaugurated on the South London line in 1909, between Victoria and London Bridge, but this has since been converted to the third rail system.

The title " South Eastern & Chatham Railways' Managing Committee" was adopted by the amalgamated South Eastern and London, Chatham & Dover Railways in 1899, but this was a fusion of traffic arrangements and rolling stock only ; the two companies retained their separate identity until the end of 1922. It is now termed the Eastern section of the S.R. system. Although the Canterbury and Whitstable line had been opened since 1830, and the Greenwich Railway, as far as Deptford, from 1836, the first to be opened in the metropolis, the London & Dover line of the South Eastern Railway was not completed from Redhill to Dover Town until February, 1844. The Bricklayers' Arms branch, with a passenger station adjacent to the Old Kent Road, opened in 1844, was intended to afford relief to London Bridge, but not attracting the traffic anticipated, the station was closed for passengers in January, 1852, and thereafter used as the London goods depot. The South Eastern opened to Charing Cross in 1864, and to Cannon Street in 1866.

From the first it was apparent that the original main line, running south to Redhill before turning east, provided a very circuitous route to Dover and other places, and to furnish a more direct line, the Tonbridge line through Sevenoaks was opened in May, 1868. This reduced the distance to places east of Tonbridge by 12½ miles, and brought Dover to within 76½ miles of Charing Cross. The Sevenoaks tunnel, of 3,451 yards, is on this line.

Between Folkestone and Dover, the engineering work is of considerable magnitude. Across the town of Folkestone the line is carried by the Foord viaduct of 19 arches, over 100ft. high, and next by means of cuttings through the Warren. Then follow three tunnels : the Martello, Abbot's Cliff and Shakespear, the latter consisting of two parallel bores—one for each line. A serious landslide occurred in the Warren during the War, and resulted in the line between Folkestone and Dover being closed for a long period.

The North Kent line through Woolwich and Dartford to Gravesend, where it joined the Rochester & Gravesend Railway, was opened in 1849, and extended from Strood to Maidstone in 1856, where it connected with the branch from Paddock Wood, on the main line.

The lines from Canterbury and on to Ramsgate and Margate were completed in 1846. Westwards the extension from Redhill through Guildford to Reading was finished in August, 1849.

Exceptional engineering works are encountered on the North Kent line, including, besides many cuttings, tunnels at Blackheath, Higham and Strood, the two latter being adjacent and having a combined length of 3,753 yards. Heavy gradients are also found on both the Tonbridge direct line and the Hastings branch.

The London, Chatham & Dover Railway started its career as the East Kent Railway. This small line opened from Strood to Faversham, gradually extended along the North Kent Coast, through Canterbury to Dover, which was reached in 1861. From 1859 the East Kent became known as the L.C. & D.R. and, by extending its system to London, provided a second and shorter route to Dover than its rival, the S.E.R. Passing through St. Mary Cray, Bromley and Penge, its first London terminus was Victoria, opened in 1863, and by a line from Herne Hill reached Ludgate Hill in 1864, and Holborn Viaduct in 1874, while the St. Paul's terminus dates from 1886. A junction was effected with the Metropolitan Railway at Farringdon Street in 1866.

As the L.C. & D.R. had to be built as cheaply as possible it is, in the matter of gradients, the heaviest road of any railway out of London. It is a succession of switchbacks varying from 1 in 100 to 1 in 132. There are two tunnels of considerable length—Shepherds-well, 2,376 yards, and Sydenham Hill, 2,200 yards. To reach the City stations there are parallel bridges across the Thames, 933ft. long at Blackfriars, and the approach to Victoria by the Battersea bridge, which measures 740ft.

Among the branches made by the L.C. & D.R., were the Seven-oaks from Swanley 1862, to Maidstone, 1874, and to Ashford, 1884. Several lines on the London district were made in the 'sixties, a branch to Gravesend in 1886, and the Catford loop line, opened in 1892.

CHAPTER XI

THE LONDON TRANSPORT BOARD RAILWAYS

AS from Saturday, July 1st, 1933, passengers on the Underground railways, trains, trolley-buses, as well as motor-buses, were notified that all these undertakings had been vested in the London Passenger Transport Board. This change in the ownership, administration and working of the transport system of London puts under one control the greatest urban transport system in the world, combining undertakings previously being under both company and municipal ownership. Ninety-two concerns were taken over, comprising 5 railway, 17 tramway, 62 omnibus, 4 coach, and 4 subsidiary

G 2

undertakings, the last including the Lot's Road Power House, at Chelsea. The five railways were the Metropolitan, District, City & South London, Central London, and London Electric (Bakerloo, Piccadilly and Hampstead Tubes).

It was in January, 1863, the initial section of the Metropolitan from Paddington to Farringdon Street, the first underground railway in the world, was opened to traffic ; and at the end of 1890 the inauguration of the City & South London gave London both its first electric railway and its first Tube.

The first portion of the Metropolitan Railway was laid with mixed gauge track, and worked by the Great Western Railway with broad-gauge stock. This arrangement, however, soon terminated, and after working the line for a time with stock borrowed from the Great Northern Railway, the Metropolitan provided their own standard gauge engines and carriages. To mitigate the smoke nuisance in the tunnels, in 1861 some experiments were made with a fireless engine, but ordinary steam locomotives were employed until electric traction was adopted in 1905.

Near the heart of the City, Farringdon Street was chosen as the terminus on the vacant site of the City Cattle Market, which had just been removed to Islington. Extensions eastward were to Moorgate in 1865, and westward, in 1868, to Gloucester Road, whilst the District Railway, which was at the commencement worked by the Metropolitan, was opened to Westminster Bridge at the end of 1868, and to Blackfriars in 1870.

The junction with the Great Northern line at King's Cross was completed in October, 1863, and in 1864 the Hammersmith line was opened with broad-gauge trains running to the City. A junction with the Midland Railway at King's Cross was effected in 1868, and the way for extension to the country was initiated by the opening of the St. John's Wood Railway in 1868 from Baker Street to Swiss Cottage. Until 1883 this branch was single track with a passing place at St. John's Wood.   The main line was extended through the City to the Great Eastern Railway terminus at Liverpool Street in 1875, and from Bishopsgate to Aldgate in 1876.   Bishopsgate Station has been renamed Liverpool Street.   The completion of the last link of the Inner Circle Railway was not completed—Mansion House to Aldgate—until 1884, although the short piece from Aldgate to the Tower was opened in 1882.   The temporary station at the Tower was closed on completion of the Circle.   Before this the St. John's Wood line had reached Harrow, in 1880, Pinner, in 1885, and Rickmansworth in 1887.   The Aylesbury extension was opened to Chesham in 1889, and to Aylesbury in 1892, after taking over the Aylesbury & Buckingham Railway (Aylesbury to Verney Junction) the previous year.   The Harrow & Uxbridge line was opened in 1904.   This line was one of the first sections to have an electric service, which was inaugurated on January 1st, 1905.   Later developments were the taking over of the Great Northern & City line from Finsbury Park to Moorgate, and the inauguration of an electric service over the East London Railway through the Thames Tunnel, completed by Brunel in 1843, when it was used as a public highway.   Recent extensions are short lines from Sandy Lodge to Watford, and Wembley Park to Stanmore.

The Metropolitan Railway's generating station was at Neasden, where the repair and car sheds were also situated.

The history of the lines formerly known as the " Underground " as distinct from the Metropolitan may be said to start with the opening of the D.R. from South Kensington to Westminster in 1868.   Extensions eastward to Blackfriars and westward to West Brompton soon followed and, as already stated, the trains for the first few years were worked by the Metropolitan.   On the opening of the Mansion House extension in 1871, the District started operating its own trains. By 1884 they were running to Putney Bridge, Richmond, Ealing and Hounslow.   Connections with the West London line, near Addison

Road, enabled trains to be worked from the Mansion House to Broad Street via Willesden and Hampstead, and to Moorgate via Westbourne Park. A junction was also made with the G.W.R. at Ealing, and from 1883 to 1885 a through District service was operated between Mansion House and Windsor, not stopping between Ealing and Slough.

On the opening of the Whitechapel & Bow Railway, in 1902, through running to Barking was started, and in 1932 the electric service was extended over the L.M.S. to Upminster.

The electrification of the District line was taken in hand soon after some comparative tests had been made in 1900, between Kensington High Street and Earl's Court. A temporary power station was built and the line electrified between the two stations. Trials between a standard steam engine versus electric motor coach were carried out, and the latter won. The line from Ealing to South Harrow, completed in 1901, was never operated as a steam line, and was opened for traffic as the first section of the electrified D.R. in June, 1903. The Hounslow and South Acton service was the next to be converted to electric working, and thereafter the change-over was much more rapid. The last D.R. steam trains were withdrawn on November 5th, 1905. Combined with the installation of electropneumatic signalling by electric working, the services have been speeded up throughout. The journey time from Ealing to the Mansion House in steam days was 48 minutes, whereas to-day a " non-stop " does it in 30.

The City & South London Railway has the distinction of being not only the pioneer " tube " railway, but also of being the first electric railway in Great Britain, barring the small Volk line on the beach at Brighton. From the opening on December 18th, 1890, until its total reconstruction which began in 1922, the line was operated by electric locomotives. The original three miles from King William Street to Stockwell was soon extended both north and south. The first extension was from the Borough to Moorgate, opened in February, 1900, and the original tubes under the Thames, which had no station at London Bridge, were abandoned, as was also the old terminus at King William Street. The Stockwell-Clapham Common line was opened three months later. By the end of 1901 the line had reached the Angel Station, Islington, and Euston in 1907.

In 1913 the C. & S.L.R. was amalgamated with the Underground railways, and arrangements made for a connection with the Hampstead line at Euston, and for the tunnels to be enlarged from 10ft. 6in. diameter to 11ft. 8¼in., to take standard tube rolling stock. From August, 1922, the line from Euston to Moorgate was closed, and the rest of the line in November, 1923, for the reconstruction. This was completed and practically a new line opened on December 1st, 1924, and since known as the City Railway. By means of the Camden Town—Euston loops, trains had been running from Edgware and Highgate to Moorgate from April of that year. The line from Clapham Common was extended to Morden in 1925.

The Central London Railway was opened on June 27th, 1900, by King Edward VII (then Prince of Wales), and had a length of 5¾ miles. For three years heavy electric locomotives were used to haul the trains, but they caused too much vibration, and motor coaches were substituted.

In July, 1907, the uniform twopenny fare, which was responsible for the popular name " Tuppeny Tube," gave way to graduated fares. To serve the Franco-British Exhibition of 1908 the Central London line was extended to Wood Lane, and four years later the important section from the Bank to Liverpool Street was brought into use.

In 1911 sanction was obtained for a connecting line at Wood Lane to link up with the proposed Ealing & Shepherds Bush line of the G.W.R. Work on this was delayed during the war and it was not until August, 1920, that trains operated between Liverpool Street and Ealing. Many of the stations have been remodelled in recent years, and escalators installed.

The London Electric Railway was an amalgamation carried out in 1910 of three lines—the Baker Street & Waterloo, the Charing Cross, Euston & Hampstead, and the Great Northern, Piccadilly & Brompton, known popularly as the Bakerloo, Hampstead and Piccadilly Tubes.

Work on the original section of the first of these was commenced in 1898, and good progress made for about three years, when financial difficulties prevented continuance. Authority was obtained for extensions to Paddington and the Elephant, and the line as between Baker Street and Lambeth North was opened on March 10th, 1906 ; four months later it was extended to the Elephant. Baker Street did not long remain the terminus, and the Paddington extension was completed and opened for traffic in sections : to Marylebone in March, 1907 ; Edgware Road, June, 1907 ; and Paddington, December 1st, 1913.

To link up with the then L. & N.W.R. the line was extended to Kilburn Park and Queen's Park in 1915, and since 1917 through trains have operated between Elephant & Castle and Watford Junction.

The Great Northern, Piccadilly & Brompton Railway was hailed at its opening as London's longest tube railway. It was opened from Finsbury Park to Hammersmith and between Holborn and Aldwych in 1906.

Further developments were the opening of the extension from Finsbury Park to Arnos Grove, in 1932, to Enfield West, and to Cockfosters in 1933.

The Charing Cross, Euston & Hampstead Railway was commenced in 1903, and opened between Charing Cross and Golders Green and Highgate, with a junction at Camden Town, in 1907. Hampstead has the distinction of being London's deepest tube station, being 200ft. below the surface. An extension of this line northwards to Edgware was completed as far as Hendon (Central) in November, 1923, and to Edgware in August, 1924.

The Camden Town junctions between the City & South London and the Highgate and Edgware branches of the Hampstead line having been opened in April, 1924, the two railways have since been operated as virtually one system. To link up the southern end of the Hampstead line with the C. & S.L. an extension was made from Charing Cross to Kennington, in September, 1926, and at the same time, through-running over the C. & S.L. extension to Morden was brought into operation.

The District and its allied lines take current from the Lots Road Power House, Chelsea. This has forty boilers and ten turbo-generators, with a total output capacity of 150,000 kilowatts.

CHAPTER XII

SMALLER BRITISH RAILWAYS

THERE are still a few independent, small lines, some of standard gauge and some of narrow gauge, on most of which steam locomotives work the traffic. The Easingwold Railway—$2\frac{1}{2}$ miles in length—leaves the London & North Eastern Railway main line at Alne, a few miles north of York, and, as its name implies, runs to the small market town of Easingwold. It possesses one locomotive and one passenger carriage, and can therefore claim to be our smallest standard gauge passenger line. Another small offshoot of the L. & N.E.R. is the North Sunderland Railway, from Chathill to Seahouses, on the Northumberland coast. This is four miles long, and is now worked by a Diesel locomotive.

Other independent lines are the 24-miles long Kent and East Sussex, from Headcorn, on the Dover main line of the Southern Railway, through Tenterden, to Robertsbridge, on the Tonbridge and Hastings line ; also the 19 miles East Kent Railway from Shepherdswell, near Dover, to the new Kentish colliery district.

There is one railway in this country, with a regular passenger service, where a ticket cannot be purchased, because they are issued free of charge ; moreover, it is a State Railway, and of standard gauge. This is the Woolmer Instructional Military Railway, and is operated by the Royal Engineers as part of their railway training. It runs from Bordon, where connection is made with the Bentley and Bordon line of the S.R., through some of the prettiest forest scenery in Hampshire to Longmoor Camp, a distance of about five miles. From Longmoor it has been lately extended further south for another $3\frac{1}{2}$ miles to Liss, on the Guildford and Portsmouth section of the S.R. With the exception of about a mile in the vicinity of Longmoor, which has been doubled, for the training of the Royal Engineers in double-line operation, the line is single throughout. The depot at Longmoor is extensive, with a number of sidings and well-equipped workshops. Here also are situated the administrative offices of the railway, signalling school, and the barracks of the R.E. railway companies.

The regular service of trains between Bordon and Longmoor consists of six trains daily in each direction, but these are little patronised by the general public. Goods trains are also run for the carriage of coal, forage, ballast, timber, etc.

The peace establishment at Longmoor comprises 22 officers and 385 other ranks. In the summer, officers and men of the supplementary reserve recruited from the four main railways undergo a fortnight's training here ; this reserve is made up of 54 officers and nearly 3,000 other ranks. The rolling stock consists of six locomotives and over 100 carriages and wagons, all kept in spick and span condition.

Most of the narrow gauge railways in this country are to be found in the mountainous districts of North Wales, where they are used for bringing slate from the quarries, but some of which are used considerably as holiday attractions. The Festiniog Railway, the gauge of which is 1ft. 11½in., and its associated Welsh Highland Railway—31½ miles in all—is probably the most interesting, with all its carriages painted different colours. It connects the quarries of Blaenau Festiniog with the sea at Portmadoc, and then takes a northerly route through the famous Pass of Aberglaslyn and Beddgelert, along the foot of Snowdon to Dinas Junction, a few miles south of Caernarvon. The Vale of Rheidol line, of the Great Western, from Aberystwyth to the Devil's Bridge, is of the same gauge, and also the Lynton & Barnstaple line, of the Southern. The 15in. gauge Eskdale Railway, from Ravenglass, on the Cumberland coast, to the village of Boot, on the slopes of Scafell, has several locomotives, which are miniature replicas of standard main line engines, to work its trains.

The Romney, Hythe & Dymchurch 15in. gauge line runs from the western end of Hythe town, passes through the seaside village of Dymchurch to New Romney, with an extension to the lighthouse at Dungeness. The locomotive stock of this interesting little railway comprises five Pacific type engines, in general outline similar to the standard express locomotives of the L. & N.E.R., and two Mountain, or 4-8-2 type, for the heavy excursion trains, as well as two 4-6-2 engines which are miniature replicas of Canadian Pacific Railway engines. Most of the carriages are of the semi-open type, seating two passengers aside, but there are also some covered carriages for the winter traffic. The line has a double track, and on the straight stretches a speed of 25 miles an hour is attained.

The Snowdon Mountain Railway, the only rack-rail line in the kingdom, is quite a curiosity. Rising by gradients as steep in places as 1 in 5, the train climbs the mountain at the rate of five miles an hour. The Swiss-built engine, with its mechanism for working in the rack-rail, and its boiler set at an angle to the frames, has an exceedingly curious appearance. The ingenious arrangements by which perfect safety is assured include an air-compressing appliance for retarding the train when descending, and automatic governors which apply the brakes and shut off steam when the speed exceeds five miles per hour, and an apparatus which effectually prevents either locomotives or carriages from jumping the rail. The carriages have open sides, and are not coupled to each other, nor to the engine, which is always below them. Double fastenings are fitted to the doors, as in places the railway runs on the edge of a precipice, having a sheer drop of hundreds of feet. The views as the mountain is ascended are truly fine, provided the weather is clear. The summit level is 3,140ft. up.

CHAPTER XIII

IRISH RAILWAYS

CONSIDERING its small population, the lack of industries, and practically no mineral wealth, the railways of Ireland have developed to a larger extent than seemed probable at one time, although at a slower rate than here. Opened in 1834, the earliest railway of importance was the Dublin & Kingstown. Later the section between Kingstown and Dalkey, opened in 1844, was worked for some time on the atmospheric system. Irish like, the gauge had to be different, and 5ft. 3in. was fixed as the standard for main lines, but there are now numerous small lines, some of considerable length, with the rails only 3ft. apart.

The Ulster Railway followed the Dublin & Kingstown, being brought into use from Belfast to Lisburn in August, 1839, and completed to Armagh in March, 1848. It now forms part of the Great Northern Railway, which owns the main line between Dublin and Belfast.

The locomotives of the Irish railways are smaller than those of this country, in spite of the liberal construction gauge, and the trains generally are not so fast. Yet the best trains show some exceptionally good running, and compare favourably with many in Great Britain.

The mileage of the broad-gauge track is under 3,500 miles, and of the narrow-gauge about 250 miles.

The largest system, the Great Southern Railways, has been formed by the amalgamation, in 1924, of 13 railways, the three largest of which were the former Great Southern & Western, Midland Great Western, and Dublin & South Eastern Companies. Four other small broad-gauge systems and six narrow-gauge were included in the group. Although certain economies in working have been effected, improvements have been made in the train services since the fusion, and the rolling stock has been brought up-to-date by the provision of new locomotives, bogie carriages and dining-cars ; and the permanent way has been strengthened on the main routes.

The Great Southern ranges over the whole of the former kingdoms of Munster, Leinster and Connaught ; from Dublin it serves the commercial centres of Waterford, Cork and Limerick, and goes to Galway and Sligo.

The far western section, from Farranfore to Valentia, where the Atlantic cables start, is one of the most picturesque in the world. At a height of over 100ft. above the sea, the railway clings to the side of the mountain with cuttings or embankments, and crosses mountain gorges, on its way to Valentia, the most westerly station in the British Isles.

The fastest services on the main line are the Dublin—Cork mail trains, and the Cork and Rosslare boat trains. The 4-6-0 engines used were built with four cylinders, but lately these have been replaced by two large ones, to reduce the number of moving parts. The works at Inchicore, Dublin, is the largest locomotive establishment in Ireland. One of the latest developments in railway work on the Great Southern is the Drumm battery train, which runs between Dublin

2–10–4 OIL-BURNING FREIGHT LOCOMOTIVE, No. 5905, CANADIAN PACIFIC RAILWAY.

Built at the Montreal Locomotive Works for working heavy freight and passenger trains over the Rocky Mountains, these powerful machines are fired by oil. They are fitted with a booster auxiliary engine applied to the second pair of wheels on the four-wheeled trailing bogie for use when starting and on the heavy grades. It has two cylinders, 25½in. bore by 32in. stroke ; coupled wheels, 5ft. 3in. diameter. The working pressure is 275 lbs. per sq. in. In working order the engine weighs 202 English tons. The tractive effort is 77,200 lbs., to which the booster, when in operation, adds another 12,000 lbs.

2–8–4 BOOSTER-FITTED LOCOMOTIVE, No. 720, SOUTH AUSTRALIAN GOVERNMENT RAILWAYS.

Built at the Government Railways shops at Islington to suit the 5ft. 3in. gauge, the powerful locomotives of the " 720 " class have two cylinders, 22in. diameter by 28in. stroke. The coupled wheels are 4ft. 9in. diameter. The boiler, which carries a working pressure of 215 lbs. per sq. in., has the large heating surface of 2,975 sq. ft. and a grate area of 59.5 sq. ft. The tractive force with the booster working is 52,000 lbs. The total weight in working order of engine and tender is 233 tons 8 cwts.

2–8–2 FREIGHT LOCOMOTIVE, WITH MECHANICAL STOKER, H.E.H. THE NIZAM'S STATE RAILWAYS.

This is one of an order for freight locomotives built in Glasgow for India, and although the mechanical stoker is in common use in the United States, this is the first installation of British manufacture. As to the reasons for incorporating this device the work of firing a powerful modern locomotive is exceedingly hard, a consideration of importance in firing in a tropical climate. The leading dimensions are : cylinders, 22½in. diameter by 28in. stroke ; coupled wheels, 5ft. 1½in. diameter ; boiler pressure, 180 lbs. per sq. in. Tractive effort, 35,264 lbs., and an additional 7,923 lbs, when the booster is working. Weight of engine and tender, 176.7 tons.

4–8–2 LOCOMOTIVE, SOUTH AFRICAN RAILWAYS.

These South African engines are exceedingly powerful for the 3ft. 6in. gauge, and compare very favourably with those of many broad gauge systems of other countries.

The powerful and efficient example shown was built by the North British Locomotive Company of Glasgow. Engines of this type are used to work coal trains of 700 to 800 tons on the outward journey from Germiston over the Germiston-Witbank section in the Transvaal—a length of 80 miles.

They have two cylinders, 24in. diameter, with a stroke of 26in., and the valve gear is of the Walschaert type. The boiler pressure is 185 lbs. per sq. in. ; heating surface, 2,510 sq. ft. ; superheater area, 466 sq. ft. Grate area, 40.5 sq. ft. Driving wheels, 4ft. 3in. diameter. Total weight of engine and tender in working order, 148 tons. Tractive force, 40,744 lbs.

TWELVE-COUPLED LOCOMOTIVE, No. 9016, UNION PACIFIC RAILROAD.

Huge as the machine illustrated is, it calls for less manual effort from its crew than one of our largest British locomotives, possessing, perhaps, half its hauling powers. It was specially designed for the Union Pacific Railroad by the American Locomotive Co. for a service of fast freight trains to take the place of large " Mallet " type locomotives of maximum haulage power but lower rates of speed.

The total length of engine and tender over couplers is 102ft. 6in. ; the extreme height is 16ft. 1½in. over the dome, and the greatest width, 11ft. 2in.—dimensions which are far and away beyond anything permissible on British railways, quite apart from the weight of 26½ tons on each of the coupled axles.

The tractive power of this enormous engine is 96,650 lbs.

2–8–8–2 SINGLE-EXPANSION ARTICULATED LOCOMOTIVE, No. 252, WESTERN PACIFIC RAILROAD, U.S.A.

Among the largest and most powerful locomotives in the world, the 2-8-8-2 articulated engines built by the Baldwin Locomotive Works for the Western Pacific Railroad are used for hauling fruit trains of 3,500 tons between Oroville and Portola, California, through the Feather River Canyon. With a steam pressure of 235 lbs. per sq. in., the tractive effort is 137,000 lbs.

There are four cylinders, each 26in. diameter by 32in. stroke ; the driving wheels are 5ft. 3in. diameter. The weight of the engine in running order is 297 tons, and the total weight of engine and tender is 480.6 tons. Oil is used as fuel.

2–10–4 FREIGHT LOCOMOTIVE, No. 854, CHICAGO GREAT WESTERN RAILROAD.

This locomotive has five pairs of coupled driving wheels, with a very large boiler and grate area, and is used for heavy freight service. The rear truck is fitted with an auxiliary booster engine and a mechanical stoker. By the adoption of new metals it has been possible to lighten the reciprocating and revolving parts, eliminating unnecessary weight in the running gear and utilizing it for greater boiler capacity.

The " Corn Belt Route " is the trade mark of the Chicago Great Western, as it serves the food-producing states of Kansas, Missouri, Iowa, Nebraska, Illinois and Minnesota.

2–8–8–0 SIMPLE " MALLET " LOCOMOTIVE, No. 3700, PENNSYLVANIA RAILROAD.

Although this locomotive follows the Mallet principle of articulation, it is peculiar in that simple expansion is used for all four cylinders instead of the usual two-stage expansion, with the low-pressure cylinders located on the rear mobile group. This non-compound arrangement simplifies the design by keeping identical the four cylinders, pistons, etc.

The cylinders are each 30½in. diameter, with a 32in. stroke. The driving wheels are 5ft. 2in. diameter. The tractive effort is 135,000 lbs. Weight of engine and tender in working order 354½ tons (British).

H

and Bray. The train is driven by electric motors, the current being furnished from a storage battery, which is claimed to last six times as long as the ordinary type, and is not so heavy.

Kingsbridge Station is the main Great Southern terminus in Dublin, but other termini are Harcourt Street and Broadstone.

The Great Northern system extends from Dublin, in the south, to Belfast and Londonderry, in the north. It reaches Warrenpoint and Newcastle in an easterly direction, and Bundoran, on the shores of the Atlantic, on the west, with a mileage of 562. It also owns jointly with the L.M. & S.R. the County Donegal Railway, a narrow (3ft.) gauge line of 110 miles. The most important engineering work on the main line is the viaduct over the River Boyne, at Drogheda. It is 90ft. above the water, and has a centre span of 265ft. and two of 140ft. each. The Great Northern provides an excellent express service between Dublin and Belfast, and the fastest running times in Ireland are in force on this section. The best train between Dublin and Belfast covers the distance of 112 miles in 2 hrs. 20 mins., including stops at the principal stations; the run between Dublin and Dundalk, 54½ miles, occupies only 54 minutes.

The rolling stock of this system is well up to modern standards, about 60% of the locomotives being fitted with superheaters. Although most of the locomotives are of moderate size, the latest three-cylinder compound express engines are powerful machines, with a high-working pressure, and have given every satisfaction on the accelerated main line services, to counterbalance the stop made for Customs examination at the Free State frontier.

In the north the Northern Counties Committee of the L.M. & S.R. serves Belfast, Larne, Portrush, Coleraine and Londonderry. Until recently the N.C.C. trains from Belfast to the Londonderry line had to reverse at Greenisland, a very inconvenient arrangement, as it meant a change of engines. A loop line has now been constructed, three miles in length, avoiding Greenisland and providing a clear run. On this loop is the largest reinforced concrete railway viaduct in the British Isles. It is 630ft. long, and consists of three large arches of 89ft. span, with a number of approach arches on either side of 35ft. span. Following the completion of this fine piece of work, a very smart and well-equipped buffet car train was started to provide a fast service for Portrush residents whose business interests are in Belfast. Known as the " North Atlantic Express," it leaves Portrush at 8.10 a.m., and arrives at Belfast at 9.30 a.m. The evening return train leaves Belfast at 5.15 p.m. and arrives at Portrush at 6.35 p.m. The distance is 65¾ miles. The carriages on this train are fitted up on similar lines to those of the " Royal Scot " train of the L.M. & S.

Passengers for Ireland from England and Scotland on landing from the Stranraer boat at Larne Harbour are run by non-stop express trains of the N.C.C. to Belfast, via Carrickfergus.

The north-east corner of Ireland is served by the small Belfast & County Down Railway, 68 miles in length. Bounded on the north by Belfast Lough, on the south by the Mourne Mountains, and on the east by Strangford Lough and the Irish Sea, it is a busy line and has a large seaside traffic, besides serving a good residential district on the Bangor line, and was very prosperous until quite recently.

CHAPTER XIV

CONTINENTAL RAILWAYS

WHEREAS the railways of this country have been built by private enterprise, most of those of the Continent have been constructed, or subsidised, by the State, and have been laid out either to facilitate trade intercourse or as military lines for defence purposes. Fortunately, the latter requirement does not exist in the British Isles —thanks to the sea being our frontier. In France, Spain and Portugal the main lines are not actually owned by the State, and there are important lines owned by companies in Holland, Sweden, Luxembourg and Switzerland, but they are, to a certain extent, subject to State control.

In France the Northern, Eastern, Paris—Orleans (with the Midi), and Paris, Lyons and Mediterranean systems are operated under a system of concessions, but there are two State-owned railways, the French State Railways and the Alsace-Lorraine Railways. The two principal Spanish Railways—the Madrid, Zaragoza & Alicante, and the Northern—are also worked by Companies under concessions. In Germany, Holland and Belgium the railway systems have been formed into managing companies in which the State interests are vested.

Many of the Continental railways have been laid out as main trade routes, to develop the resources of the countries ; consequently, there are practically no competitive routes, with the result that train services are fewer and slower as compared with this country. There are, however, some notable exceptions, and due to the competition of road motors, there has been during the past fifteen to twenty years a big effort to improve train services, not only in frequency but in speed and comfort. The finest development is found in France and Germany. Italy is making marked progress in railway communication, and, owing to its lack of coal and the presence of an abundant source of supply of energy from water power, has encouraged the development of electrification. Spain and Portugal, as well as Russia, have cut themselves off from the systems of other countries by adopting gauges of 5ft. 6in. and 5ft. respectively, for their railways, and no trains can run through.

The first striking difference between a British railway station and a Continental one is the very low platforms, and this has the effect of making the locomotives and trains look much larger when seen from the lower level. At many stations, too, it is customary for a train arriving to discharge its passengers before the entraining passengers are allowed on the platform. Therefore, the booking-hall, waiting-rooms and refreshment buffets, etc., are arranged to communicate with a single entrance to the platform.

There are some very fine stations in the Continental cities. The magnificent central terminal at Milan is a wonderful specimen of architectural display. The total cost, including the locomotive and goods depots, is estimated at £11,000,000. It was opened by the King of Italy in 1931. The station has been constructed on the two level principle ; the lower " story " is devoted to the handling of goods and mail. Traversers and hoists to the upper level facilitate disposal of the wagons, although two of the twenty roads have direct communication with the station yard. The high level passenger station has twenty-two roads, and each road has two platforms, one for passengers and the other for luggage and all operations connected with the working of trains. The large roof spans are of similar type to those at Paddington ; the span of the largest is 235ft.

Amongst the biggest terminals are the new station of the Eastern Railway, and the St. Lazare station of the State lines in Paris. The Eastern terminus has thirty platform-roads, converging into nine running roads. There are ten main line departure lines, twelve middle roads for suburban trains, and eight main line arrival roads. The handsome façade of the main building is 600ft. long.

An outstanding feature of railway services on the Continent is that they are generally the same on Sundays as on week-days, and all timetables are arranged on the 24-hour system.

The heavy Paris suburban traffic on the State Railways is dealt with by trains of nine double-decked all-steel bogie cars worked on the " pull-and-push " principle, by engines of the 2-8-2 type. The locomotive pulls the train into Paris, and pushes them out, the driver taking his place in a special control compartment at the head of the train. This method of operation is also used on the Nord and P.L.M. services.

H 2

The great Central Station at Leipzig, in Germany, into which run all the railways serving the town, is another very large and fine station.

Germany claims to have the fastest train in the world. This is the " Flying Hamburger," which is really two Diesel-electric cars coupled together, with a bogie between, streamlined, to reduce the resistance of the air. It carries 102 passengers, and has a buffet. It covers the 178 miles between Berlin and Hamburg at an average speed from start to stop of 77.4 m.p.h. On the same line the fastest steam train in Europe now runs at an average speed of 69.4 m.p.h.

On the State Railways of France the daily railcar service from July to September, between Paris and Trouville—Deauville, non-stop in both directions, in 2 hours for the 136.2 miles, represents an average speed of 68.1 m.p.h., start to stop.

Germany has the biggest railway mileage in Europe, with about 38,750 miles of track, followed by France with 33,000 miles, and Russia, with nearly the same mileage. Belgium, with about 5,000 miles of track, claims to have a greater mileage of railways per head of the population than any other country.

A glance at the map of Europe will show that Switzerland, with its great Alpine barriers, lies across several of the most important Trans-European railway communications. The direct routes from London and Paris to the Balkans, to the near East and Italy, cross the country, and the problem of getting the railways through the mountains by practicable gradients has involved remarkable engineering work, and the piercing of the Alps by the great tunnels of the Simplon and St. Gothard, to enable the direct routes to be followed. From France there are two main routes, one from Paris and Dijon to the Simplon, via Lausanne or Berne, the other up the Rhine from Paris or Brussels to Mulhausen, and through the St. Gothard, via Lucerne, or alternatively to the Simplon by way of Berne and the nine miles Loetschberg tunnel. The other main route of importance is via the

Arlberg tunnel from France and Belgium, through Basle and Zurich, for Innsbruck, Vienna, Budapest and Roumania.

Although at the moment Great Britain holds the record for average high steam railway speeds, France is hardly behind us in the number of trains timed at high speed. The Northern Railway is the fastest line in the world for the number, as no less than sixty-six of its daily trains run from start to stop at 55 m.p.h. or over, thirteen of them exceeding the mile-a-minute rate on the Paris—Belgium road. The longest non-stop runs on the Nord are to the Belgian cities of Liège and Brussels. The 229.9 miles from Paris to Liège are run by the 10.10 a.m. "Nord Express" from Paris in 3 hrs. 50 mins., an average of 59.4 m.p.h., and the 193.2 miles to Brussels, Midi, 3 hrs. 15 mins. by the 11.25 a.m. "Etoile du Nord." The "Golden Arrow" non-stop Pullman train takes 3 hrs. 10 mins. to cover the 184.1 miles to Calais Maritime, but the "Rapide" which stops at Etaples is timed at 3 hrs. 5 mins. only—63.4 m.p.h.

The fastest train on the Nord is the 1.36 p.m. out of Paris, which is timed at 65.2 m.p.h. for the 95.7 miles to St. Quentin on the Brussels road.

The main line of the Paris, Lyons & Mediterranean Railway for the 196 miles between Paris and Dijon, which carries all the fast trains to Vintimiglia, Belfort, Vallorbe, Geneva and Modane, is one of the most heavily loaded sections in the world, since between 6.30 and 11 p.m. every night eighteen express trains leave the Gare du Lyon for Dijon and beyond. They are normally run at ten-minute intervals, but when the traffic is heavy, before holidays, etc., as many as thirty expresses leave Paris at five- to six-minute intervals.

The famous "Cote d'Azur Rapide" has been speeded to cut three-quarters of an hour on its former schedule from Paris to Marseilles. It now starts at 8.15 a.m. from the Gare du Lyon and takes 9 hrs. 33 mins. to cover the 536.3 miles—56.4 m.p.h.

Most of the famous express trains of the various European railway systems are maintained by the International Sleeping Car Co. It inaugurated the " Orient Express " as a through train of sleeping and restaurant cars between Paris and Constantinople. In June, 1883, it ran for the first time between Paris (Est) and Vienna, and was made up of bogie sleeping cars, a six-wheeled restaurant car, and vans, all belonging to the International Company. By the linking up of the Serbian and Roumanian railways a through rail route was established to Varna, thence by boat to Constantinople ; Constanza was substituted eventually for Varna. An all-rail journey was later made via Belgrade, the train running through to Constantinople three times per week, as well as twice via Constanza. In 1901 a connection with through cars was made with Berlin, via Wels, in Austria. It was this train which gained notoriety during the war, as it was run by the German, Austrian and Bulgarian railways as the " Balkan-zug," and was looked upon as the forerunner of the German idea of a Berlin-Bagdad express. This was not to be, although since the war the International Co. has extended its services across the Bosphorus to Angora and Asia Minor, with motor coach connections to Bagdad. At present there are three through express trains making the trans-European run to the Near East, i.e. the original Orient express, now Paris-Vienna, 860 miles in 20.10 hours ; speed, 43 m.p.h. ; the Arlberg-Orient Express, Paris-Vienna, via Basle and the Arlberg tunnel, 926 miles in 22.45 hours, speed 40 m.p.h. ; and the Simplon-Orient Express, which runs from the Gare du Lyon, Paris, via Lausanne and the Simplon tunnel to Milan, thence via Venice, Trieste, Zagrib, Vinkovei, Belgrade, Sofia, etc., to Constantinople. At Vinkovei the cars for Bucharest are detached, and at Nisch the train is divided into a portion for Athens and a part for Constantinople (now Istanbul). From Paris (P.L.M.) to Athens totals 2,173 miles, and occupies 62.15 hours, the speed approximating 35 m.p.h. By the other portion of the same train the journey of 1,899 miles, Paris to Istanbul, is covered in 58.18 hours, the speed averaging about 32 m.p.h.

Other important trains of the International Co. include the " P. & O." Express, which runs once a week between Calais and Marseilles, 732 miles in 18.40 hours, or a speed of 39 m.p.h., but before the war the time occupied was only 16.35 hours. Further East the " Taurus Express," which is an extension of the Simplon-Orient, makes direct connection with Syria and Iraq via Aleppo—a point 881 miles from Haidar-Pasha on the Asiatic side of the Bosphorus. From Aleppo this train continues to the port of Tripoli, whence it is only a two hours motor run to Beyrout and a six hours journey to Haifa. Here train is again taken to Cairo—a distance of 3,847 miles from London, covered in 6 days, 1 hr. 20 mins.

The " Trans-Siberian " train-de-luxe between Moscow and Irkutsk, and eventually extended to Vladivostock, was started by the International Co. in 1898. After the Russian Revolution of 1918 the rolling stock was confiscated by the new rulers of the country. This train is now operated by the Russian Soviet Railways Administration.

CHAPTER XV

COLONIAL AND INDIAN RAILWAYS

AS early as 1837 the colonists of British Guiana proposed to build a railway from Georgetown to the Mahaica River, but it was not until 1848 that the first length of six miles was opened. This was not only our earliest Colonial line but also the first railway on the South American continent. This small line has since been extended, and is now owned and operated by the Colonial Government.

The next colony to build railways was Ceylon, which were established seventy years ago. The first section from Colombo towards Kandy was opened in 1865, and completed in 1867. After a gradual rise the railway climbs into the mountains, reaching an altitude of 6,226ft., the ruling grade of this section being 1 in 44, with five chain curves. The adoption of the 5ft. 6in. gauge was presumably copied from the Indian standard, but for the feeder lines in the mountainous districts the 2ft. 6in. gauge was found more suitable. Of these feeder lines, the most interesting is that from Nanu Oya Junction to Regalla, passing Nawara Eliya, the health resort of the island. An elevation of 6,315ft. above sea-level is reached, with gradients of 1 in 23 and curves of 70ft. radius. Combined with a rainfall in the mountains averaging 200in. per annum, the operation of the railways is somewhat difficult.

In Malaya the first line was built by the Government of the State of Perak, and was opened in 1885. Since then there has been a steady growth in the mileage of the Federated Malay State Railways, of metre gauge, and they now connect with the Siamese Railways, with through dining and sleeping car trains for the 1,000 mile journey from Singapore to Bangkok. It is of interest to note that these international trains on the Siamese section are invariably hauled by powerful 4-8-4 Diesel locomotives. These are changed at the Siamese frontier, and the run thence to Singapore is behind a three-cylinder 4-6-2 steam locomotive of the F.M.S.R.

In British West Africa the Sierra Leone Railway opened in 1898 is of 2ft. 6in. gauge, as opposed to the usual African 3ft. 6in. It has a main line from Freetown, the capital, extending over 200 miles, nearly to the frontier of Liberia, and several branches.

For the Gold Coast Colony the 3ft. 6in. was chosen for its system of about 500 miles. The principal lines are from the harbour at Takoradi, on the Gulf of Guinea, to Kumasi, the capital of Ashanti, mostly through dense tropical forest with trees 60ft. to 100ft. high, and from Accra, the capital of the colony, on the coast, to join the other line at Kumasi.

Passing on to Nigeria, the railway system formerly comprised two disconnected systems based on Lagos and Port Harcourt. An extension of the Eastern line made connection with the main line from Lagos to Kano, at Kaduma Junction. There is no rail to the town of Lagos itself, the terminus of the Western line of the railway being on Iddo Island, where there are wharves for smaller ocean craft and barges ; the deep-water wharves for the mail boats are at Lagos itself. New wharves have recently been made at Apapa, on Iddo Island, on the opposite shore of the lagoon to Lagos, and a branch railway has been extended over a stone causeway from the mainland at Ebute Metta. The Nigerian system now comprises some 1,700 miles of 3ft. 6in. railway, with its headquarters at Ebute Metta, where fine new workshops have been constructed.

The South African Railways, which serve an area five or six times the size of Great Britain, form one of the largest State owned systems in the world. The lines are laid on a standard gauge of 3ft. 6in., which carries some of the heaviest locomotives and rolling stock. Many of the locomotives, in running trim, weigh as much as 170 tons, while the main line coaches are equal to British types in proportion. The " Union Express "—one of the South African trains-de-luxe—does the journey of 900 miles between Cape Town and Johannesburg in 28 hours. The merits of the performance can be appreciated when it is recalled that the route rises from sea-level at Cape Town to an altitude of close upon 6,000ft. at Johannesburg, and that the mountain sections traversed contain many formidable gradients and curves. All the main lines leading from the ports of Cape Town, Mossel Bay, Port Elizabeth, East London and Durban have very steep grades, and curves as sharp as 300ft. radius are frequent. There are about 12,000 miles of 3ft. 6in. gauge, and 700 miles of 2ft. gauge track.

In East Africa the metre gauge has been adopted for the Kenya and Uganda Railways. Powerful " Mikado " type engines work the mail and heavy goods trains from the Port of Mombasa to the capital,

Nairobi, 330 miles, but the gradients are so heavy that the time allowed is 17 hours, and the same engine goes through, although the drivers and firemen change over half-way. Beyond Nairobi the line extends to the Nile, near Lake Victoria, Nyanza, and is worked by eight-coupled Garratt locomotives.

On the Tanganyika Railway wood fuel is used by the engines, which are usually of the 4-8-0 type, and of metre gauge.

The Rhodesian Railways have a very large coal traffic from the Wankie mines, near the Victoria Falls of the Zambesi, the trains being largely worked by Garratt, or 4-8-0 type engines. Built to the 3ft. 6in. gauge, the Rhodesian lines connect with the South African system from Vryburg to Buluwayo, and run from the latter city to the Rhodesian frontier, where connection is made with the Portuguese line to the port of Beira. Another section goes north to the Congo Free State.

The railways of Nyasaland had one peculiarity in their construction. Other African railways extended inwards from the sea ; the first Nyasaland railway was built inland, and later extended outwards to meet the sea. The original line stretched from Blantyre to Chiromo, on the Shire River, a tributary of the Zambesi. Communication was maintained by steamers with Chinde, at the mouth of the Zambesi. But the Shire started to get shallow, so the railway had to be pushed further down the river to Port Herald. It got shallower still, and so a further length was made, this time to the Zambesi itself, at Chiromo. Then, after the war, it was decided to complete the railway to the sea, and the Trans-Zambesia Railway was built, connecting Murraca, on the opposite bank of the Zambesi, to Chindio, and thence to Dondo, on the Beira Railway, 17 miles from the port of Beira itself. The final links in this chain have now been forged by the completion of the Lower Zambesi Bridge, $2\frac{1}{2}$ miles in length, which connects the Central Africa and Trans-Zambesia Railways, and by the extension inland of the Nyasaland Railway from Blantyre itself to Lake Nyasa.

Australia and New Zealand have a variety of gauges for the railways, each colony adhering to its original gauge. Both the South Australian and Victorian lines are to the 5ft. 3in. gauge, so that trains can run through from Adelaide to Melbourne, but between the other states the breaks of gauge at the frontiers waste time and money, as all goods and passengers have to be transferred. The gauges of the different systems are : New South Wales, 4ft. 8½in. ; Victoria, 5ft. 3in. and 2ft. ; South Australia, 5ft. 3in. and 3ft. 6in. ; Queensland, 3ft. 6in. and 4ft. 8½in. ; Western Australia, 3ft. 6in. ; Trans-Australian Railway, 4ft. 8½in. Queensland has laid down a 4ft. 8½in. gauge track from the New South Wales frontier to Brisbane, so that the Sydney express can now run right through.

In New South Wales the main lines have many difficult grades. At about 20 to 70 miles from the sea are various ranges of mountains which have to be climbed by the trains out of Sydney to reach the inland tableland. In the vicinity of Sydney a big scheme of electrification has been carried out.

Queensland is a sheep-raising country, with sugar and fruit plantations, and has a long mileage of 3ft. 6in. gauge track.

Between Kalgoorlie, in Western Australia, and Port Augusta, in South Australia, runs the Trans-Australian Railway, 1,050 miles in length. Over the Nullabor Plain, 385 miles of its track are dead straight and level, the longest stretch without a curve in the world.

The railways of New Zealand are worked very much in accordance with British practice, but heavy gradients make the lines difficult to operate. The gauge is only 3ft. 6in. and the construction gauge somewhat restricted, yet the latest Pacific and Mountain type locomotives handle trains of observation saloons and dining-cars over banks as steep as 1 in 40, and sharp curves at fairly high speeds. On the North Island some six-cylinder Garratts run the mail trains at 50 m.p.h. on the level. On this section is the Makatote viaduct, the highest bridge in New Zealand, 320ft. high and 800ft. across ; and also the Raurimu spiral, where the line makes four complete turns in four miles at a grade of 1 in 50. On another line, from Wellington to Napier, the Rimutaka incline called for a grade of 1 in 15, one of the steepest ascents in the world to be worked by ordinary adhesion. It is operated on the Fell system, the locomotives having an extra pair of horizontal wheels gripping a central third rail.

India, with an area more than twenty times that of Great Britain, and a population of some 320 millions, is served by a railway system of 41,700 miles, of which about one-half is on the 5ft. 6in. gauge, approximately 17,200 miles on the metre gauge, and the balance of 10% of narrower gauges. It is a land of contrasts, with immense plains, some fertile, and others deserts, being made fertile by irrigation works. These plains stretch from the seaboard to the Himalayas.

The broad-gauge metals of the North Western Railway stretch from the Khyber Pass, beyond Peshawar and to Quetta, through the Bolan Pass, and connect the Imperial capital of India, Delhi, with the port of Karachi. It has also a number of narrow gauge feeder lines of 2ft. 6in. gauge—notably the Kalka-Simla line, which serves the summer capital of the Government, 7,000ft. above sea-level.

The great centres of India are widely separated. Bombay, the nearest port to England, where most of the best trains start or finish, is 794 miles to Madras, 839 to Cawnpore, 885 to Lucknow, 865 to Delhi, and 1,400 miles to Calcutta.

From Calcutta to Tuticorin, in the south, is 1,700 miles. From the latter place to Peshawar will take best part of a week.

The mail trains are particularly heavy, as there are separate provision for Europeans and natives, and females have separate accommodation. There are also pilgrim specials to the various famous religious resorts, at certain periods of the year.

Both of the main lines of the G.I.P. (the one to Jubbulpore, and the other to Nagpur) are handicapped by the long Ghat inclines of 1 in 37, to surmount the mountains running parallel to the West

Coast, but all traffic to and from Bombay over these gradients is now worked by electric traction. The goods trains of the G.I.P. run up to 1,000 tons behind the tender, and are usually worked by powerful 2-8-0 or 2-8-2 engines.

The Bengal-Nagpur Railway mail trains are worked by four-cylinder compound Pacific type locomotives. For their heavy coal trains of 2,300 tons, they have the most powerful engines in India—Beyer-Garratts, with two eight-coupled units, and weighing 234 tons apiece. They handle these trains over a hilly section of 260 miles.

The fastest train on the G.I.P. is known as the " Deccan Queen," now worked by electric locomotives for the whole of its journey. The " Imperial Indian Mail " goes across country to Calcutta via Jubbulpore in 42 hours, starting immediately after the arrival of the P. & O. steamer at Bombay. It is sometimes known as the " Blue Train of India."

The " Frontier Mail " to Peshawar covers the run as far as Delhi at an average of 38 m.p.h. by the Bombay-Baroda & Central India Railway route.

The East Indian Railway with headquarters at Howrah, Calcutta, passes through the richest and most populous parts of India, the main line traversing the Ganges Valley.

A most interesting line is the Darjeeling Himalayan Railway, of 2ft. gauge. Darjeeling is the summer station for Europeans living in Calcutta. This tiny railway rises to a height of over 7,000ft. above sea-level, with very heavy gradients and remarkable curves. Particularly interesting are the spirals along the spurs of the hills. In one place two complete turns are made in a small area, accomplishing a rise of 140ft. by so doing. At another place is a zigzag, the train entering a dead end and then reversing up another gradient to another dead end, whence it goes forward on its journey.

CHAPTER XVI

AMERICAN RAILWAYS

IN the same year that the Stockton & Darlington Railway began working, in 1825, the first steam locomotive ran in America. Built by Colonel John Stevens, the projector of the Pennsylvania Railroad, it operated on a circular track on his estate at Hoboken, New Jersey. In 1835 there were 1,098 miles of railway in the United States, and by 1860 this had increased to 30,635 miles. Following the Civil War there was a period of rapid railway construction, and the opening of the twentieth century found nearly 200,000 miles of railway line. The present mileage is about 240,000 or, roughly, one-third of the world's total. Over 2,000 miles of the railways are electrified. There are about 65,000 locomotives, 53,000 passenger cars, and 2,350,000 freight cars in the United States.

A railway joining the Atlantic and Pacific coasts was discussed long before it was practicable to deal with such a tremendous project. The first line across the States from the Missouri to the Pacific was proposed in 1861 by a few merchants of Sacramento, California. Their project was to build a line to the eastern boundary of California, to be known as the Central Pacific Railroad, and there to meet a line extending westward from the Missouri, later known as the Union Pacific Railroad. The western section presented formidable difficulties, as it involved crossing the Sierras of Nevada at an elevation of 7,000ft., and traversing a desert for nearly 700 miles.

In 1862, Government support was assured and a start made at Omaha, on the left bank of the Missouri. Work was slow, as no railway had reached Omaha, and all material had to come up from St. Louis by water. By the end of 1867 the track was laid over 500 miles west of the Missouri, and the Central Pacific had left the Sierras behind and were crossing the desert of Utah. The final joining up of the metals took place near Ogden in April, 1869, and the inauguration took place on May 10th, when two silver spikes and two of gold were driven home, to complete a task that opened a new era in the history of the United States.

The Pennsylvania Railroad is the largest system in the United States, measured by the freight and passengers carried. Its charter dates from 1846, and the main line from Philadelphia over the Allegheny Mountains to Pittsburg was opened in 1852. It became apparent that the best country to the west could only be opened up by railways, and the Pennsylvania acquired interest in lines extending from Pittsburg to Chicago, St. Louis, and other growing cities. Additional lines were built laterally into the Southern States, and northward to the Canadian border. Prior to 1871 the eastern terminus of the Pennsylvania Railroad was still the City of Philadelphia. In that year it extended its services to New York, on the New Jersey side of the Hudson River. In 1903 it began the work of tunnelling the Hudson River, and in 1910 opened the Pennsylvania Station, in the middle of New York, with tunnels extending eastward across the city, and underneath the East River, to connect with the Long Island lines. In 1917 it opened the Hell Gate Bridge route, by which New England is afforded a direct rail route to the Middle States, West and South. At present the Pennsylvania is engaged on the electrification of the line from New York to Washington, a distance of 227 miles. It is proud of being the pioneer in introducing the first de-luxe all-Pullman train in America—" The Pennsylvania, Limited." This train has operated daily between New York and Chicago since 1881, and was the forerunner of the " Broadway, Limited," and other famous trains of to-day. For over thirty years the whole of the passenger cars of the Pennsylvania Railroad have been built of steel throughout, and are absolutely unburnable.

Probably the other most important railway in the United States is the New York Central. As in the case of the Pennsylvania, this

I

system comprises a number of different lines, which have been amalgamated to form a grouped railway controlling about 12,000 miles of line.

To compete with the rival Pennsylvania for the traffic between New York and Chicago, the famous " Twentieth Century Limited," of the New York Central Lines covers the 960 miles at an average speed of 56.5 m.p.h., and is often run in three sections daily, each of twelve Pullmans. The Pennsylvania " Broadway, Limited," with a shorter but heavier road, of 908 miles, takes under 17 hours.

Another enormous railway system is the Southern Pacific, covering nearly the whole of the Western States from Canada to Mexico, and comprising about 16,500 miles of line. It is an amalgamation of the Union Pacific, Central Pacific and other lines, as well as the trans-continental line of the Southern Pacific, which had been opened in 1882. The Northern Pacific trans-continental line was completed the following year, and since then various other ways of crossing the continent have been made.

There are some very fine stations in America, and it is common practice to make one large station serve a number of lines. For size and architectural effect, the enormous New York termini of the New York Central and Pennsylvania systems in New York are probably without a rival—with, perhaps, the exception of the new Milan terminus of the Italian Railways. The magnificent New York Central, Grand Central, is the largest station in the world ; it is approached by tunnels, and built on two levels, 20ft. and 44ft. below street level. The upper one deals with long-distance trains on 42 tracks, whilst the lower has 25 tracks, for short-distance traffic ; in addition there are 62 other tracks on the two levels, for storing of rolling stock, etc. All the trains are worked electrically, the change to steam operation taking place at Harmon, 32 miles out.

The really fast long distance train in America originated in New York—the " Empire State "—for it was on October 26th, 1891, a new train known as the "Empire State Express" left New York City for the 437½ miles run along the Hudson River to Buffalo, in 8 hrs. 40 mins., averaging over 50 miles an hour, and reaching a speed of 70 m.p.h. on part of the journey.

Since May 29th, 1935, the world's record for the fastest start to stop run made by a steam-worked train has been held by the stream-lined "Hiawatha" Express of the Chicago, Milwaukee, St. Paul & Pacific Railroad for the 43.1 miles from New Lisbon to Portage, at an average speed of 73.9 m.p.h., compared with the 71.4 m.p.h. of our G.W.R. "Cheltenham Flyer" from Swindon to Paddington.

The train leaves Chicago at 1 p.m. and covers the 410 miles to St. Paul in 390 minutes (6½ hours), including five stops. The south-bound train is also due out of St. Paul at 1 p.m. and it is on this run that the 73.9 m.p.h. average, mentioned above, is attained.

In size and power the average American locomotive far exceeds anything we have in this country, due largely to the liberal dimensions of their loading gauge. Here the maximum available height is 13ft. 6in., but the Americans have 16ft., and sometimes 16ft. 6in., in which to build their rolling stock, and ample width, although their gauge is the same as ours. Roughly, the largest American engines are more than twice the size, weight and tractive effort of the biggest working in Great Britain.

Modern all-steel passenger cars in America run to 75 or 80 tons in weight, or twice that of the average British coach, therefore a 12-car train will amount to 1,000 tons, as against the 500 to 600 tons of the heaviest expresses here.

The centre corridor type of open carriage is almost universal in America, and as so many journeys are made by night, most of the long-distance trains are provided with sleeping accommodation. At night the seats are pulled out to form lower berths, and sections of the underside of the car roof are lowered to make the upper bunks on either side of the centre gangway. On certain trains, however, the English type of compartment sleeping cars are coming into use.

In handling freight traffic, the methods of the American railways are far ahead of our country. The average wagon in use is mounted on bogies, and vehicles intended for carrying minerals often have a capacity for a load of well over 85 British tons, which, by comparison, makes the 20-tonner here a mere toy. In fact, on the Virginian Railway, taking coal from the mines to the seaboard, 12-wheeled bogie wagons carry no less than 107 tons of coal each, and on arrival at Sewell's Point, where the coal is shipped, these enormous vehicles are lifted bodily and the contents discharged into the vessel's holds.

Then, the whole of the rolling stock is equipped with automatic centre couplers, and their use is universal on freight stock. The dangerous work of coupling by hand when shunting is entirely eliminated by their adoption, and, further, the general use of continuous power brakes enables the heavy tonnage to be operated with safety.

The Canadian Pacific is the older of the two large railways of Canada. The Government granted its Charter in 1881 for a railway from the Atlantic to the Pacific. Work commenced on it simultaneously at Ottawa, at Winnipeg, and on the Pacific coast, and on November 7th, 1885, at Craigellachie, the rails from the east and west were joined up. Leaving Montreal, passing round the northern shore of Lake Superior, and across the prairie to Winnipeg and Calgary, the line crosses the Rocky Mountains by heavy grades, the summit being reached at an altitude of 5,329ft. It descends by the Kicking Horse Pass to the Columbia River Valley, and then climbs again to cross the Selkirk range, through the Connaught Tunnel, 3,800ft. up, after which the line drops to Revelstoke, 2,519ft. The crossing of the Gold Range by the Eagle Pass is followed by the down grade to Vancouver, 2,898 miles from Montreal. During recent years some of the heavier sections of the original line in the Kicking

Horse Pass, and over the Selkirks, have been re-aligned and gradients reduced, necessitating the construction of two corkscrew tunnels, as well as the five mile bore of the Connaught Tunnel.

The other Canadian line is the Canadian National, with 22,675 miles of railway, the largest railway in the world, although it has only 1,200 miles of double road. It is an amalgamation of the Grand Trunk and Canadian Northern systems. From Halifax, Nova Scotia, the main line to Quebec crosses the river St. Lawrence by one of the biggest bridges in the world, with a span of 1,800ft. From Quebec it passes on to Montreal, Ottawa and Winnipeg, where it takes a more northerly course than the Canadian Pacific, crossing the Rocky Mountains by the Yellowhead Pass, the only summit, 3,712ft. above sea-level. The line then descends by the North Thompson River and Fraser River valleys to Vancouver, 3,775 miles from Halifax, the longest railway in the world with the exception of the Trans-Siberian Railway. Originally the Western Terminus was at Prince Rupert, 550 miles north of Vancouver. The Canadian National Railway operates a daily service between Montreal, Toronto and Vancouver by the " Continental, Limited " train.

CHAPTER XVII

PASSENGER AND GOODS ROLLING STOCK, BREAKDOWN TRAINS AND SNOW PLOUGHS

CARRIAGE STOCK.—Both for day and night travel our railways provide rolling stock which in point of comfort reaches a standard unsurpassed anywhere. Efficiently sprung carriages, comfortable and tasteful upholstery, and heating, lighting and ventilation are carefully studied.

Air-conditioned carriages on day and night expresses are being

12

introduced.   Hairdressing saloons, as well as radio facilities are to be found on some expresses, whilst on certain of the London—Leeds trains of the L. & N.E.R. a cinematograph van, fully equipped for exhibiting sound films, is provided as a regular feature.

Early railway passenger carriages were four-wheelers.   In 1838 when accommodation was introduced for third-class passengers, the vehicles were simply open trucks, without seats.   Although coverings were soon afterwards provided, open third-class carriages were running until well on in the 'fifties.   It was in 1838 that the London & Birmingham Railway put into service the first coach fitted with a mail pick-up device ; this was a net somewhat similar to that still used on Post Office vans.

Six-wheeled coaches were experimented with by the G.W.R. in the later 'fifties, although an eight-wheeled saloon was built for Queen Victoria in 1848.   Nowadays carriages are mounted on two four-wheeled bogies, though sometimes six-wheeled bogies are used.

Oil lamps were used in the early days, not to give light for reading, but to enable passengers to see sufficiently well for entering and leaving ; for reading, the passenger provided a candle.   By 1863 coal gas was used for lighting on the North London and Metropolitan Railways.   It was stored in collapsible bags, or bellows, which were carried in the guard's van, or on the roofs of the carriages.   Compressed oil gas became widely adopted as a satisfactory illuminant in the 'nineties, although the London & North Western began to use electric train lighting in 1887.   Electricity is now the standard, on account of less risk of fire in accidents.

The introduction of restaurant and sleeping cars and Pullmans represent the most striking developments of late years.   Most of these are of the open type, and this type of vehicle is also used on the London Underground Railways, and on some of the electric trains of the L.M. & S. and L. & N.E.R., but not on the Southern Railway suburban electric trains.

In 1928 the Great Western and L.N.E. and L.M. & S. Companies introduced sleeping accommodation for third-class passengers on their long-distance night expresses by the provision of compartment coaches, having let-down berths above the ordinary seats to give lying-down facilities for four passengers per compartment. Many of the recent coaches are non-convertible to day use, thus allowing refinements in design to be effected. First-class sleeping cars have been run on the night expresses for many years. They were introduced on the N.E.R. in 1873, and on the Midland in the following year.

Warming apparatus was non-existent when railway travel started, but footwarmers, filled with hot water, were vessels in use in the 'fifties, and, later, these vessels contained salt, and were heated in boiling water vats prior to use. Steam warming by low-pressure steam from the engine was introduced in 1884. The "atmospheric" system, which is now in extensive use, is an improvement of recent date.

The first hot and cold shower bath to be installed on a train in this country was fitted to a first-class sleeping car in 1930.

The Pullman car provides the maximum comfort and luxury at a small extra charge on the fare. Whilst ordinary carriages are built with the latest conveniences and comfortable seating, etc., the space per passenger is necessarily somewhat limited ; the Pullman car gives one a greater sense of freedom and luxurious travel. Most of these cars have names ; some are of classical origin, etc.

Quite a number of the restaurant kitchen cars of the L. & N.E.R. have been equipped for all-electric cooking, to ensure an efficient method of preparing food on the trains.

Express freight trains run nightly and daily between main centres. Consignments conveyed by these trains are delivered the morning following despatch.

Special vehicles for the conveyance of fish, milk, coal, plate-glass, long girders, animals, scenery, motor cars, etc., are provided. The largest railway wagon in the British Isles is of the well-type, and built for carrying concentrated loads, such as electrical stators, ingots, etc., up to 150 tons in weight.   It is constructed on the cantilever principle, so that the weight is distributed over the entire length of 232ft., and it has 56 wheels.

A large stock of vans is maintained especially for the transport of bananas, which arrive principally at Avonmouth and Garston Docks, as well as London, Hull and Southampton.   These vans are insulated in summer and steam-heated for winter use, and equipped with the vacuum brake for fast running.

Up-to-date equipment is provided for the transport of foodstuffs. Hygienic 2,000 to 3,000 gallons glass-lined tanks carry milk in bulk, as well as special ventilated milk vans.   Large quantities of meat are carried by the railways in insulated vans, from Scotland, and from ports to the consuming centres.   Express trains of refrigerator vans are run at frequent intervals, and ventilated and insulated containers are also used for the conveyance of perishable commodities.

Normally about 200,000,000 tons of coal are carried annually by the British railways.   Development in wagon design has been to increase the carrying capacity both in volume and weight, as compared with the weight of the wagon itself when empty.   Twenty-ton wagons are now largely used for coal traffic, and many of these are of the bottom-discharge type.   Bogie wagons of 40 tons capacity are used for shipment of coal in Northumberland, and of 50 tons load for the brick traffic from the Peterborough district, with a tare weight of under 17 tons.   The number which can be loaded in one of these wagons is from 17,500 to 20,000, according to the size of the bricks. The whole sides are made to drop, to facilitate loading.   Trains of 80 coal wagons, with a gross weight of over 1,500 tons, are worked from Peterborough to London—about 76 miles—by heavy 2-8-0 engines, and these are among the longest and heaviest operated in this country.

BREAKDOWN TRAINS.—For dealing with the derailment of vehicles, erecting bridges, loading and unloading consignments of heavy goods, etc., the railways provide a number of steam breakdown cranes at principal centres. A typical example is that stationed at Stratford, on the L. & N.E.R. The crane will lift 35 tons to a height of 28ft., and the job can be completely rotated under load. In running order it consists of three units—the crane unit, and two guard trucks. It will travel from one place to another under its own steam while at work, if necessary, and is fitted with an electro-turbo generator and complete electric lighting equipment. The crane weighs 80 tons, and the complete equipment is 93ft. long.

RAILWAY SNOW PLOUGHS.—In countries where snowstorms are of rare occurrence, and where the average snowfall is of but moderate depth, the wedge-shaped plough, propelled by two or more loco-motives, usually suffices to clear the track. But if deep drifts form, they have to be charged repeatedly, and it sometimes happens that plough and locomotives get stuck and must be dug out. On the Highland section of the L.M. & S.R. many of these ploughs are kept at the principal centres ; there are several at Inverness and Perth, and at Blair Athol, where the climb over the Grampians starts. Rotary snow ploughs, driven by steam from a locomotive boiler, are a regular part of the equipment of the North American Railways, and there are quite a number on the Continent of Europe, particularly Norway, Sweden and Switzerland, but there is seldom a downfall of snow here sufficiently heavy to call for these machines.

CHAPTER XVIII

TRAIN-FERRIES, BRIDGES, TUNNELS, SIGNALS AND PERMANENT WAY

DURING the Great War train-ferries proved their value in transporting stores and rolling stock from Richborough to Dunkerque and Calais, and from Southampton to Dieppe, direct to the Western front. In 1923 a company was organised to take over the Government train-ferry steamers for operating a permanent service between Harwich and Zeebrugge, as well as Calais, enabling railway wagons loaded at any point in Great Britain to be run direct to Continental destinations, with corresponding arrangements in ports. A service is given every night in each direction. This has now been taken over by the L. & N.E.R.

The Southern Railway has provided a vessel specially built for the carriage of motor cars between Dover and Calais, and have three train-ferry vessels ready, which are to be placed in service between Dover and Dunkerque very soon now.

BRIDGES.—Bridges and viaducts were built of brick or stone in the early days of railways, but nowadays the steel bridge is the usual form for railway requirements.

The famous bridge across the Firth of Forth is $1\frac{1}{2}$ miles long from end to end, and is the largest structure of its kind in this country. It is built on the cantilever principle, three enormous cantilever towers stretch out their arms to each other, connected by two large girder bridges. Each tower stands on a massive masonry pier, providing a base broad enough to counteract any tendency to overturn as a train runs on to the end of one of the arms. Each of the two main spans measures 1,710ft., and from the underside of the main spans in the centre to water level is 157ft., to allow the largest vessels to pass underneath. Just under seven years were occupied in constructing the bridge, and it needed 51,000 tons of steel and nearly 8,000,000 rivets to build it. The Tay Bridge, although it is two miles in length, is a much easier engineering problem. It consists of 85 steel spans, the longest of which are 245ft. across, at a height of 77ft. above water level. Another monumental bridge recently completed is that across the harbour at Sydney, New South Wales. It carries four lines of rail and a roadway having a total width of 150ft., and a clear span of 1,650ft. across the harbour, the floor being 170ft. above the water.

Bridges with a number of spans are usually termed viaducts. The Royal Border Bridge of the L. & N.E.R. which spans the valley of the Tweed, at Berwick, is 708ft. long and 91ft. above the water level, while near London the Welwyn viaduct of 40 arches is 1,560ft. long, with a maximum height of 100ft.

TUNNELS.—Most of the long British tunnels are met with on the lines crossing East and West through the Pennines, but the longest in this country—apart from the London " Tubes " tunnels—is that which runs under the River Severn, between Bristol and Newport, on the G.W.R. The river itself is $2\frac{3}{4}$ miles wide, but so that the approach gradients should not exceed 1 in 100, it was necessary to construct a tunnel 4 miles 624 yards in length. Owing to serious floodings of the workings, it took 13 years to complete the tunnel. One of the earliest British tunnels—at Kilsby, on the L.M. & S. main line— was also flooded out when the workings broke into an underground quicksand, and pumping machinery had to be put down before the work could proceed.

The tunnels through the Pennines on the L.M. & S.R. are the Totley, Cowburn and Disley respectively $3\frac{3}{4}$, 2 and $2\frac{1}{2}$ miles long, on the Sheffield and Manchester line, and on the L. & N.E.R. line between the same cities the two single line tunnels at Woodhead are 3 miles in length. The L.M. & S. line from Huddersfield to Manchester passes through Standedge Tunnel, 3 miles, with three parallel bores—one double line and two single.

SIGNALS.—Safety in railway travel in Great Britain is largely due to the efficiency of the signalling arrangements. When trains were few and far between, they were worked on a system of " time intervals." A train was allowed to proceed with caution a few minutes after the preceding train had passed a signal, and at full speed after a longer period had elapsed. Semaphore signals were used with the " arm " capable of being placed in three positions ; horizontal meant a dead stop, slanting allowed the train to proceed with caution, and in the dropped position, in line with the post, it was a " clear " road, and full speed ahead allowed.

When the electric telegraph came into use, and with it the " block " system, the two-position signal arm was adopted. The line is divided into what are called " block " sections, each controlled by a signal box. The rule is that two trains shall not be allowed on the same line of rails within the same block at one time. Movements of the train are controlled by the signals worked from each box, and communication from box to box is made by a code of bell-signals or by instruments giving a visible indication.

The semaphore signals used here always point to the left of the post, facing the driver on the engine footplate, and that side of the arm is painted red or yellow with a white or black stripe at the outer end ; the back of the arm is white with a black stripe.

There are two main kinds of signals, first those with square ends to their arms which indicate that a driver must stop if at danger ; and secondly, those which have arms cut into the shape of a fish-tail, which are " distant " signals at which a stop is not imperative. At night, stop-signals are indicated by a " spectacle," with red and green glass moving in front of a fixed white lamp, showing a red light when at danger, and a green one when pulled off. Distant signals now show a yellow light in the " on " position.

The colour light signal is slowly ousting the semaphore signal from our railways. The chief advantage is that by reason of the powerful electric lights employed, a clearer indication in bright sunlight and in times of fog can be given than with the semaphore signal. Further, it allows for a number of different aspects to be exhibited beyond the " stop " and " proceed " indications given by the semaphore signal. These aspects are provided by using three different colours, viz. : red, yellow and green, and by combinations of these colours, as required.

PERMANENT WAY.—Great care is devoted to the laying of the permanent way of the British railways, the smoothest riding in the world. By far the most important item is the rail itself. These are rolled from steel ingots in rolling mills, and the type almost exclusively used here is known as the " bull-head " section, weighing for main line work 95 lbs. to 100 lbs. to the yard. For branches and subsidiary services, 85 lbs. per yard is sufficient. As to length, 45ft. is the usual, although the L.M. & S.R. have laid stretches of track with 60ft. rails to reduce the number of rail joints, but they are awkward to handle. The principal requisite of the steel rail is resistance to wear, which means a very hard material without brittleness. At places where the traffic is heavy, as on electric railways, manganese steel or nickel-chrome steel is often used, but these alloy steels are very expensive.

Upon the sleepers are bolted the cast iron " chairs," required for supporting the bull-head rail. Into these the rails fit rather loosely, until they are packed tightly in position by the wooden wedge or " key," which is driven at the side of the rail. The rail-ends are held together on either side by a couple of tightly-fitting " fish-plates," secured to each other through the rails by four " fish-bolts." The ends of the rails are not allowed to meet, as a small space must be left for expansion in the heat of summer.

The latest practice is to use a shorter fish-plate with two bolts only, enabling the supporting sleepers, nearest the joints, to be brought closer together.

The flat-bottomed rail is standard for America, and, in fact, almost everywhere except in Great Britain. It is cheaper to lay, but the bull-head rail and chaired track has greater solidity, and needs less attention when it is laid.

The sleepers, which serve the dual purpose of holding the rails true to gauge, and of distributing the load over a wide area of ballast, are usually of hard wood, which often undergo a preserving process of treatment with creosote oil, which is a solution of coal tar which has been forced into the timber under high-pressure, rendering it resistant to weather. In some parts of the world, metal sleepers are used to defeat the ravages of white ants, or resist the effects of damp.

CHAPTER XIX

RECENT DEVELOPMENTS IN RAILWAY WORK

MANY innovations have been introduced recently in operating the intensively worked railways of this country. Foremost, possibly, is the high-speed passenger train-working. As the outcome of trial runs on the L. & N.E.R. in 1934-5, between London and Leeds and London and Newcastle, mentioned on pages 30 and 31, it was proved that a high-powered express locomotive, with a load of 200-250 tons, could maintain a high average speed by running fast uphill, without undue speed on the level or down hill. These trials made it clear that a speed-up was a practical proposition, and the first outcome was the " Silver Jubilee," Britain's first stream-lined train, which started on September 30th, 1935, running between London and Newcastle, a distance of 268 miles in four hours, with one intermediate stop at Darlington, the average speed for the 232 miles being 71 m.p.h. This has been followed by the " Coronation " train between London and Edinburgh, 393 miles, in six hours each way, started on July 5th, 1937, and the " West Riding Limited," Leeds to London and return, 186 miles, in 2 hours, 45 mins. each way, inaugurated on September 27th, 1937.

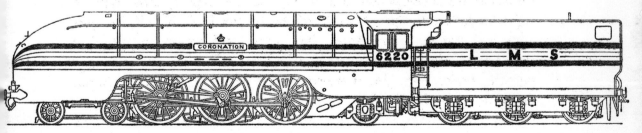

FOUR-CYLINDER PACIFIC TYPE STREAM-LINED EXPRESS LOCOMOTIVE, "CORONATION," No. 6220, L.M. & S. RAILWAY.

For these services, Sir Nigel Gresley introduced his stream-lined Pacific type locomotives, which incorporate certain improvements on the original design. These include an increase in the working pressure to 250 lb. per sq. in., and a slight reduction in the diameter of the cylinders to 18½ins. Exceptionally fast running can be credited to these fine engines, including a record of 113½ miles per hour in August, 1936, with the " Silver Jubilee " train. These engines are painted " Garter Blue," and the front end is of wedge shape, in order to throw the exhaust clear—more a device to create air currents of air deflection than true stream-lining.

Mention should also be made of the " East Anglian " train of the L. & N.E.R., between Norwich and London (Liverpool Street), completing the journey of nearly 115 miles in 130 minutes, including a four minute stop at Ipswich.

Few locomotives in this country have aroused more interest than L. & N.E.R. " No. 10,000," built under conditions of strict secrecy in 1929, and subsequently dubbed " Hush-Hush," whenever the Press could get news of it. Although it proved to be powerful, fast and free-running, it was a heavy coal consumer. It was therefore decided to remove the water-tube boiler, and substitute a boiler of the type used on the " Cock o' the North " class engines, but with a working pressure of 250 lb. to the sq. in., and convert it to a three-cylinder single-expansion engine. It has been fitted with a stream-lined casing.

To meet the need for higher speeds in freight service, there has been marked development, and a very efficient type of three-cylinder 2-6-2 tender locomotive was introduced by the L. & N.E.R. in 1936. This was named *Green Arrow*, No. 4771, and several more of its type have since been completed at Doncaster Works. With a taper pattern boiler, 6ft. 5in. diameter and 17ft. 10in. long, of similar design to the " Pacifics," carrying a working pressure of 220 lb. per sq. in., coupled wheels 6ft. 2in. diameter, and three-cylinders 18½in. diameter by 26in. stroke, the tractive effort is 33,730 lbs.

The increased development of braked goods train services is one of the most important features of railway operation, and an overnight service between points 400 to 600 miles apart has become an established fact.

The heavily graded West Highland line of the L. & N.E.R. between Craigendoran, Fort William and Mallaig is single track throughout, with limited axle loads. Its construction involved some difficult engineering feats; tunnelling has been almost avoided, necessitating wide detours around mountain sides, and heavy gradients. The trains normally loaded up to 180 and 220 tons are worked by 4-4-0 and 2-6-0 type locomotives, although during the tourist season double heading is necessary. A new type of three-cylinder 2-6-0 locomotive, built specially for this route to avoid double heading and capable of hauling 300 tons, has been put into service recently. Built at Darlington, and named *Loch Long*, engine No. 3441, has coupled wheels 5ft. 2in. diameter, cylinders 18½in. diameter by 26in. stroke, with a working pressure of 180 lb. to the sq. in. ; tractive power is estimated at 32,939 lbs.

On the London, Midland & Scottish Railway their Pacific type express locomotive, No. 6220, *Coronation*, is a truly stream-lined engine, in that its front end is designed to provide the least possible resistance through the air. Designed by Mr. W. A. Stanier, the chief mechanical engineer, and completed at Crewe, in May, 1937, in readiness to work the high-speed " Coronation Scot " train of 263 tons, between Euston and Glasgow, 401½ miles in 6½ hours, this power-ful engine is painted in a handsome livery of blue, with horizontal silver lining, to conform with the colours of the coaching stock. Leading particulars are : four cylinders, 16½in. diameter by 28in. stroke ; coupled wheels, 6ft. 9in. diameter ; boiler pressure, 250 lb. per sq. in. Tractive effort 40,000 lbs. In the course of a trial run on June 29th, 1937, from Euston to Crewe, with the " Coronation Scot " train, this engine established a speed record for the L. & M.S.R.

by attaining 112½ miles per hour. The train started regular running on July 5th, 1937, but does not run on Saturdays.

In September, 1935, the Great Western Railway introduced their high-speed train, the " Bristolian," which cut 15 minutes from the long-established two-hour run between Paddington and Bristol. On the " down " journey the route is via Bath, 118¼ miles, and the " up " run is via Badminton, 117½ miles, 105 minutes in each direction at an average speed of 67.6 m.p.h., and 67.1 m.p.h. respectively.

To improve the running of the West of England expresses two short lengths of line have been constructed to avoid passing through Westbury and Frome stations, where curves are sharp and speed restrictions have to be observed.

The Great Western added 150 locomotives to their stock during 1937, but these were all to their standard designs, which have proved efficient and reliable in service.

The Southern Railway introduced in October, 1936, the first passenger train ferry between this country and the Continent—the Dover-Dunkerque route. The service is between London (Victoria) and Paris (Nord). Three train ferry vessels have been built specially for this service, and named after Thames ferries—" Twickenham Ferry," " Hampton Ferry," and " Shepperton Ferry." Each averages about 2,840 tons, and has accommodation for 500 passengers.

Further extensions to the electrification of the Southern Railway were brought into operation on July 4th, 1937, when the services between London and Portsmouth, and Woking to Alton were inaugurated. Waterloo to Portsmouth is the longest length of track to be operated by electric traction in this country, involving 74 route miles. From Woking to Alton is 22 miles.